Studio 5000 Logix Designer

A Learning Guide for ControlLogix Basics

By

Gary D. Anderson

STUDIO 5000 LOGIX DESIGNER

A LEARNING GUIDE FOR CONTROLLOGIX BASICS

Every effort has been made in preparation of this book to ensure accuracy in presenting the many concepts, information and common usage of instructions pertaining to using the Studio 5000 Designer / RS Logix 5000 development platform. However, the information contained herein is sold without any expressed or implied warranty.

First Published: June 2016

RSLogix 5000: Understanding ControlLogix Basics

ISBN: 978-1-7341898-8-9

Contents

Preface:

The focus of this book is to look into key areas of Rockwell Automation's Studio 5000 Design software and its use in developing ControlLogix projects. These are concepts which often present a challenge to those who are new to using this platform. You may be familiar with the instruction set and programming techniques used with Allen Bradley SLC-500 or PLC-5 controllers, yet find that with Studio 5000, or earlier versions of RSLogix 5000, the same rules just don't seem to apply. If this is the case, then this book has been written with you in mind and for this purpose – to help you as a technician, make an easier transition into the PAC programming environment. My interest, and I hope yours, will be to delve into these areas that are different from many standard practices you've used when dealing with legacy PLC-5, SLC-500 or MicroLogix controllers. These differences can seem a bit awkward at first, but become easier as you gain familiarity with the software and architecture.

This book contains revisions to my earlier book on RS Logix 5000 and the ControlLogix platform. Improvements have been made in several key areas; first of all, great effort has been taken to improve illustrations and graphics, and secondly, sections have been added for topics that were not addressed in the previous book. These include sections; either new or re-written for greater clarity, on creating Add-On Instructions, on using parameters for buffering I/O; and greater clarification on the important topic of creating and using the user-defined data type or UDT. In addition to these revisions, objectives and suggestions for "*Hands-On Exercise*" labs have been placed throughout different sections, which should provide practical learning experiences linked to various topics and concepts.

As industrial automation more fully utilizes the advances made with microprocessors and programmable controllers, it has also created differences in how we develop, program, and troubleshoot a project. With the use of PAC's, such as the ControlLogix or CompactLogix controllers, we can now handle simultaneous processing events within large network domains having multiple controllers and widely distributed I/O.

Studio 5000 allows options of programming by the different methods, specified in IEC 61131-3, which include: *Ladder Logic* programming, *Structured Text* programming, *Functional Block Diagrams* (FDB), and *Sequential Function Charts* (SFC). Some of these programming methods may be familiar to you and others not so much, but clearly, there are many avenues for programming a control system to accomplish a desired result.

As I've said before, it often is not the programming that presents the greatest challenge when working with a project, but rather the practical aspects of configuration pertaining to addressing, the timing of tasks, sequencing of programs, and working with blocks of data - to name just a few. This can be especially true in those industrial environments where older PLC controllers are still widely used for the bulk of their applications. This is often the case, and makes sense given their reliability, and the fact that most technicians are very familiar with these controllers. Familiarity usually equates to ease-of-use in programming and troubleshooting, which are important factors in a production environment. Many manufacturing facilities are only now integrating PAC controllers into plant operations – even though the ControlLogix platform has been on the market for twenty-plus years. I believe a careful study of these topics should ease the learning curve needed in integrating your current programming skills with the use of Studio 5000 applications.

Although programming isn't really the primary focus of this book, there are some instructions shown which may be new to you, and many example routines shown. So my focus will be on topics; some pretty basic, which I believe build an adequate foundation for whatever type of programming conventions you decide to use.

With this in mind, here is some of what will be covered is this book:

- Why RSLogix 5000? – How it's an improvement
- Synchronous and Asynchronous control
- Integrated Architecture
- Project Organization – Tasks, Programs and Routines
- ControlLogix, CompactLogix, and GuardLogix Controllers
- Module Types and Configuration
- Understanding the Addressing Structure of Logix 5000
- Understanding Tag based addressing
- Creating Tags: Base, Alias, Produced and Consumed
- Creating and using Arrays
- Creating Add-On Instructions
- Creating User-Defined Data Types
- Creating Add-On Instructions
- Buffering I/O Data using base tags
- Buffering I/O using parameters
- Types of Faults: Major, Minor, I/O and User-Defined
- Obtaining system data – Objects & Attributes
- Fault Routines & Troubleshooting

The main premise and hope for this book remains the same as before; to build skills and familiarity with the Studio 5000 software; so that whether you are troubleshooting, designing a new project, or editing an existing routine – whatever you need to accomplish becomes an easier task.

While I think there's much to be gained by a careful reading of each section, the overall learning experience will be enhanced by taking the time to do the *Hands-On Exercise* activities as well. Having said this; I think the best approach in using the material and ideas presented in this book, would simply be to recreate some of the same examples and routines shown in the chapters that follow. This is invaluable for becoming familiar with the development software. After all, there usually doesn't seem to be much time for that, when you've been called to troubleshoot critical production equipment. Design and build a project, network with another controller, add an HMI or other network device, share information between controllers, and in general – just practice building and working with a project.

As we begin with the first section; "Why RS Logix 5000…" which focuses on the strengths of the ControlLogix architecture and its development platform, I hope you are (or become) optimistic about all the sections that follow. Each of these have been developed as logical steps toward building a solid foundation for anyone who uses ControlLogix or CompactLogix controllers, and the RS Logix 5000 / Studio 5000 development software.

WHY RS LOGIX 5000...

Advances in PLC technology over the years, together with advances in micro-processor technology, have driven automation systems to higher levels of functionality. PLC's, such as the SLC 500 and the MicroLogix family of processors, continue to be well suited for smaller automation control applications, and I believe will continue to be utilized well into the future. However, the modern PAC, such as the ControlLogix controller is far advanced by comparison. The PAC retains all the functionality of the PLC but is also able to handle plant-wide distributed control on a much larger scale. Here are but a few of the advantages of implementing a PAC versus the use of PLC legacy devices:

- Increased capability of distributed I/O.
- Real-time scan and I/O update times.
- Greatly increased user memory.
- Multiple processor capabilities with the ability to control, monitor, and communicate with multiple devices and systems.
- Advanced process control and motion control.
- Specialized dedicated tasks related to safety compliance.
- A more advanced instruction set which allows for specialized industry-specific instructions.

While legacy PLC's are still an important component used in many smaller applications, modern PAC's have taken industrial control to a higher level in terms of real-time data acquisition, high speed batch applications, manufacturing assembly lines, and large scale process control applications.

Integrated Architecture

ControlLogix processors fall within what is commonly referred to as an *Integrated Architecture* model. In very basic terms, it is the joining of operational and informational technologies into a single control package. PAC's are suitable not only for distributed I/O and motion control; but also for real-time data acquisition, monitoring of process systems, and plant-wide control. One of the overall goals of Integrated Architecture, particularly when used in an enterprise-wide application is scalability - the ability to be expanded when necessary using common network media and protocols. In other words, integrated architecture is essentially the control solution for applications where multiple processes must be monitored and controlled.

Understanding Asynchronous Control

Perhaps the most fundamental difference between legacy PLC technology and the ControlLogix platform, is the type of scan cycle employed by the PAC. You may recall that PLC systems employ a scan cycle that is sequential – completing one task, proceeding to the next, and then repeating the cycle. This is commonly referred to as a synchronous scan cycle.

Here is an illustration for the synchronous scan cycle used by most legacy PLC's such as Allen Bradley's PLC-5 and SLC-500 processors. As you can see, execution occurs in sequenced steps, ending one segment and beginning another, until the entire cycle completes and begins again.

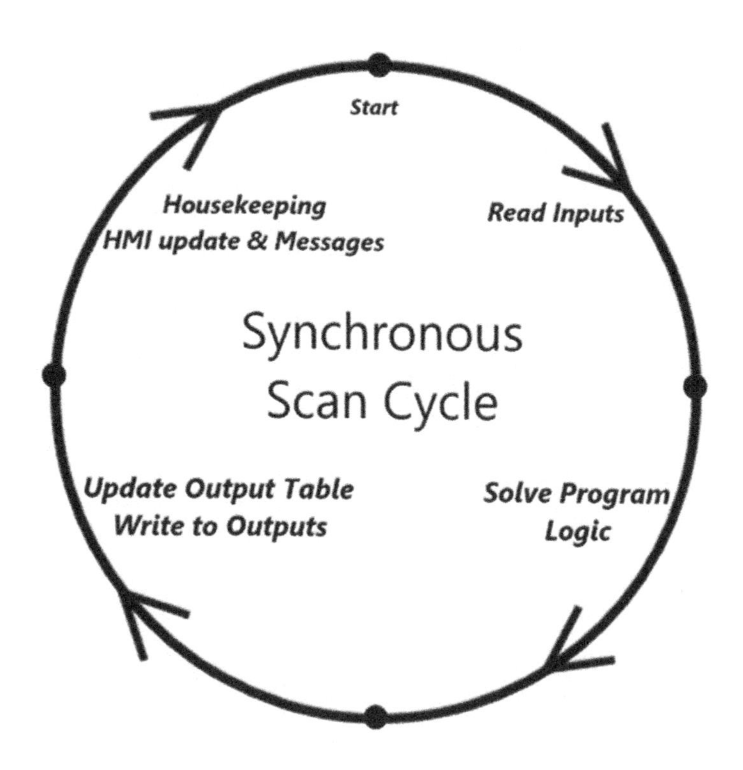

Each basic task is performed by the processor step-by-step, all tasks linked to a single clock within a single scan. These same basic duties performed during the synchronous scan are performed by a ControlLogix PAC as well, but in a much different way as far as timing is involved. This is largely due to the fact that a ControlLogix or CompactLogix system employs multiple processors, has a much larger amount of embedded user memory, and has the ability to handle thousands of I/O points.

ControlLogix employs an *asynchronous* scanning operation. Overall, asynchronous operation of the controller and its associated modules proves to be a more efficient operation - in terms of speed and data throughput. Here is a simple illustration for a PAC using asynchronous control. The arrowed circles represent the separate and differently timed cycles of the overall operation.

Asynchronous Scanning

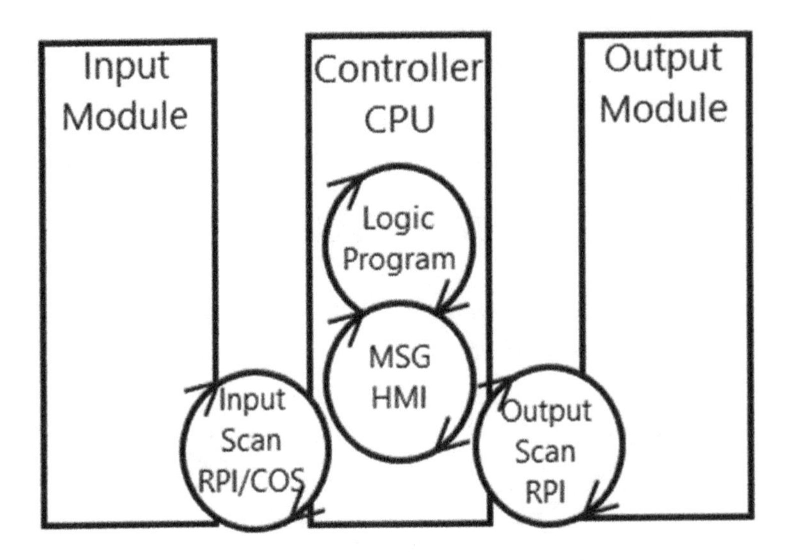

Asynchronous operation allows the controller to perform multiple tasks; sequentially, non-sequentially, and at times - concurrently. For this reason, the whole concept of "scan cycle", while still important, becomes somewhat less of an issue. Asynchronous processing is made possible by the increased speed and memory capabilities of microprocessors and also the fact that ControlLogix or CompactLogix platforms employ at least two 32-bit unsynchronized processors.

The continuous scan cycle for logic is executed as a separate operation – and updates for input and output modules operate as separate functions in their own designated time intervals rather than being part of the logic scan. Thus, in a Studio 5000 project, the more relevant issues are those pertaining to update times and the requested packet interval (RPI) settings of each input and output module. This will determine the time interval for the processor to receive input from a specific module or send signals to output devices.

While more will be discussed on the topics of RPI and RTS in later sections, a brief overview is relevant to understanding the concept of asynchronous processing. In the example shown below, I've selected a 1769-IA16 module, which is a discrete module rated for 120 VAC inputs on 16 input points. In this instance, RPI is set for individual modules as they are configured, and can range from 0.2 ms to 750 ms. As modules are selected and added to a project, a menu box allows you to configure each module. This is where you would select the slot for the module; enter a name and a short description, and set the RPI – which will configure the input module to send the status of its inputs to the controller at the RPI time period selected.

In the following example, the RPI is left at its default setting of 20 ms. So as the processor continuously executes program logic, it only receives input data from this module and updates the program, every 20 ms – when the module is set to multicast the status of its inputs. In similar fashion, an output module accepts data - the output tag table results of solved logic, according to its RPI time-value setting. At that RPI interval, the output tags from the processor are sent to the module and on to its respective field devices.

Connection

Name	Requested Packet Interval (RPI) (ms)
StandardInput	20.0 0.2 - 750.0

Here you can see the configuration menu for the selected input module – set to its default RPI value of 20 ms. More detail will be given to module configuration in later chapters.

CONTROLLOGIX CONTROLLERS:

The ControlLogix controller was introduced in 1997 as the replacement for Allen Bradley's legacy PLC's. The first controllers were referred to as L5's and were a great improvement over the PLC-5 processor in terms of program execution speed. Improvements have continued with the launch of the L6 processor in 2002, the L7 in 2010, and now the L8 controllers.

The latest ControlLogix controllers offer many enhancements over their earlier predecessors such as:

- The use of SDRAM memory
- Dual Core CPU
- An available USB port rather than the 9-pin serial port
- An SD memory card
- An Energy Storage Module (ESM) that replaces the traditional lithium battery for memory protection during a power outage.

Other differences between ControlLogix controllers and legacy PLC systems, such as the SLC-500 and PLC-5's, is the ability for having great flexibility in the placement of processors in a chassis. In the rack pictured above, you might have noticed two processors in a single rack, neither of which is located in slot 0. These types of chassis arrangements, with ControlLogix, are allowed and I/O modules are configured for each processor as needed.

CompactLogix Controllers:

CompactLogix, bulletins 1768 and 1769, are PAC controllers having a smaller modular form than the larger ControlLogix controller and chassis. These were introduced in 2006 as controllers suitable for small to mid-range sized projects.

Many of the CompactLogix controllers have imbedded I/O with the capability to expand using additional modules if necessary. The most recent evolution of the controller is the CompactLogix 5370 – L3's and the 5480 – L4's, which includes many of the same features found in the ControlLogix L7 series.

- Dual Core CPU
- SDRAM memory for faster data transfer
- USB port
- ESM rather than a lithium battery backup
- Din Rail mounting - doesn't use a chassis with a backplane but connects from side connections.

FIRMWARE REVISIONS:

Firmware is the permanent programming, sometimes referred to as the "executive program", which resides in the read-only memory (ROM) of a ControlLogix or CompactLogix CPU. Throughout the history of the ControlLogix / RS Logix 5000 platform, there have been many revisions of this embedded programming. This is often a confusing issue simply because the firmware versions of programmed project files and that of the CPU must be the same, in order to download or upload a project. For this reason, the RSLogix 5000 programming software – now called Studio 5000 Logic Designer, must agree with the firmware installed on the controller and, if going online with an existing project, the firmware of that particular project.

Since 1997, the many revisions made to the firmware have added greater functionality and performance to ControlLogix and CompactLogix controllers. Examples that showcase just a few of these evolving changes have been the ability to create *user-defined data types* (UDT's) that link multiple types of data to their specific function; the *add-on instruction* (AOI) - which is user-created logic that can be implemented as a single custom instruction in a program routine; and the ability to store comments and descriptions within the PAC memory. Again, these are only a few of the many firmware changes that have enhanced the capabilities of ControlLogix controllers and its development software.

At the same time, the necessity of performing firmware updates can often be a confusing task, possibly because the legacy PLC's which most technicians have become so accustomed to using - are still widely used, and only require a project file to be downloaded into the processor. Contrast this with the fact that, in a ControlLogix system, if a CPU needs to be changed in an existing rack or network, it will require an updated version of firmware - in addition to the logic program download.

To illustrate this, if a project was developed using RS Logix 5000 (version 18), and needed to be downloaded into a new, out-of-the-box processor having only basic firmware, such as revision 1.017, then its internal memory must be updated or "flashed" to a matching, compatible version of the project firmware – version 18.

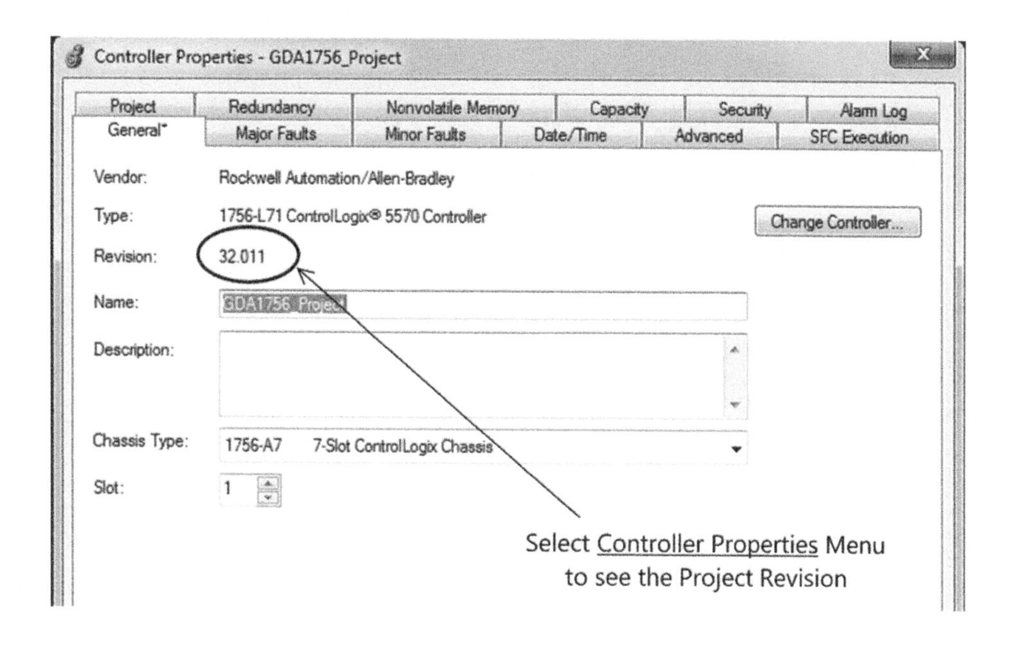

Firmware versions are downloadable from the Rockwell Automation website. An existing project can be upgraded to a newer firmware version – but not to an older version. Regardless of this however, the controller firmware must be the same as the project you wish to download. If you have your programs backed-up to a plant server or some other storage media, you can open the project, and double-click on the controller shown in the project-organizer to find its firmware version.

If you don't have a particular firmware revision, it can be downloaded from Rockwell Automation and saved on your laptop. After connecting to the new processor, you will be able to *flash* this into the embedded memory using Rockwell Automation's ControlFlash software. If ControlFlash isn't already installed on your PC, it can be installed from RS Logix 5000 installation disks or obtained from the Rockwell Automation website as a download.

USING CONTROLFLASH:

Here are basic steps for flashing a new CompactLogix processor with a different revision of firmware. In this example, the CPU - which was new and just taken out of a sealed box, had version 1.017.1 firmware. I replaced this with version 20.016 firmware, which is the same revision number as the project I needed to download to the new processor.

1. Connect with an Ethernet cable – I used a cross-over cable and the EtherNet/IP driver in RSLinx Classic.

2. Start ControlFlash > [NEXT]

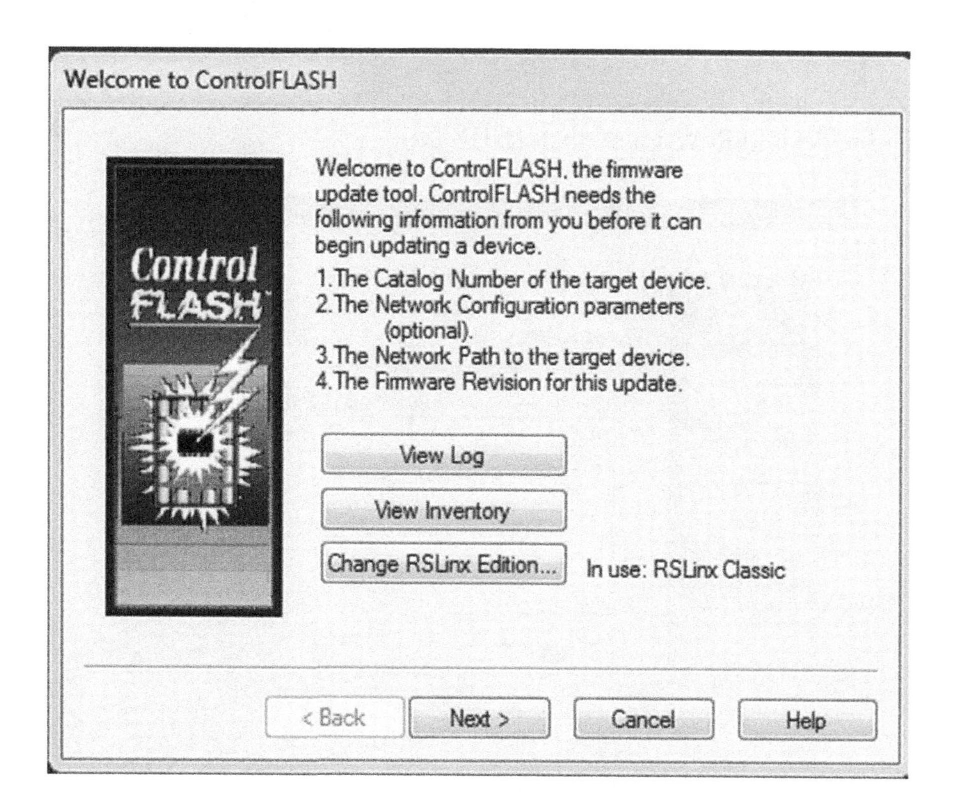

3. Select the processor to update in the project tree.

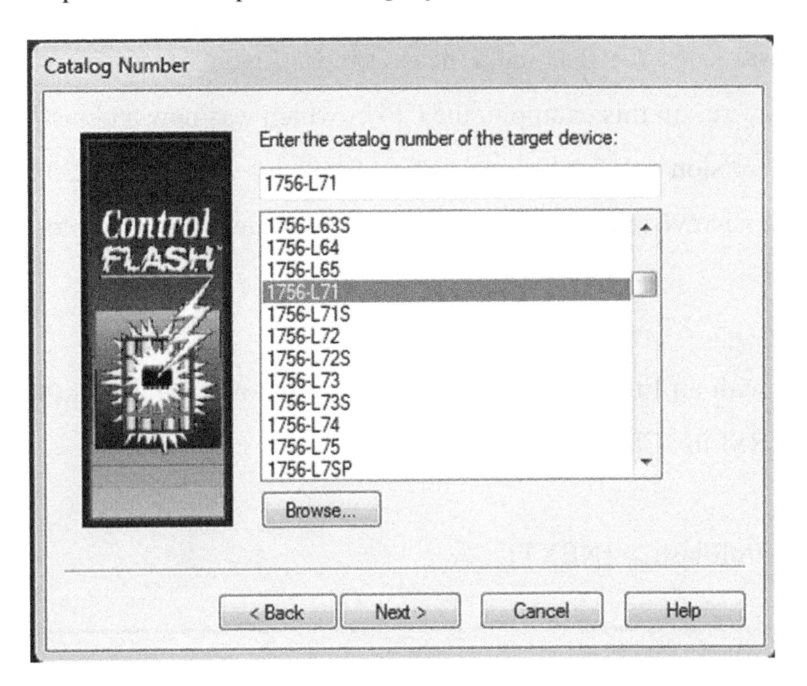

4. Select the desired Revision # then [NEXT]

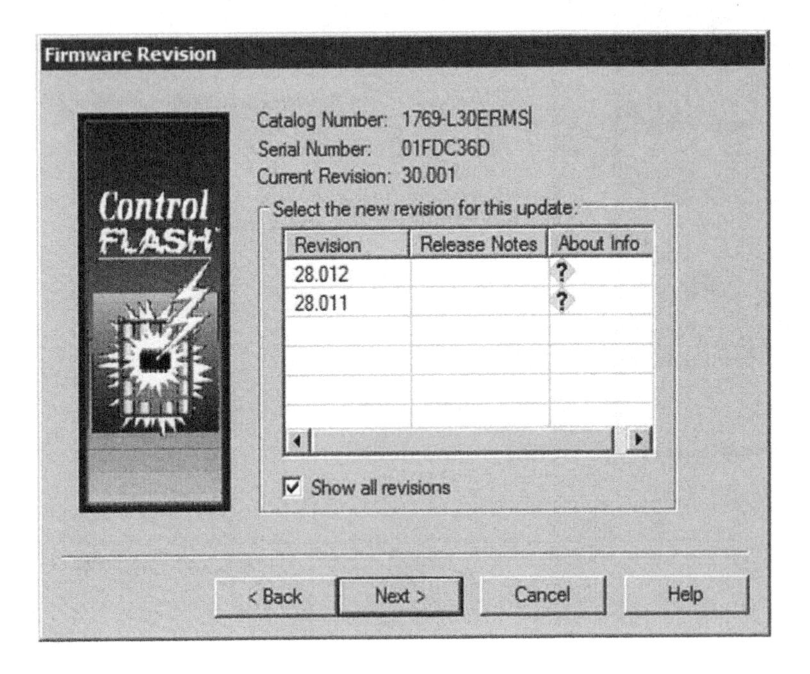

5. Do you wish to continue? [FINISH]. At this point the different firmware will write to the connected processor. After completion exit the program.

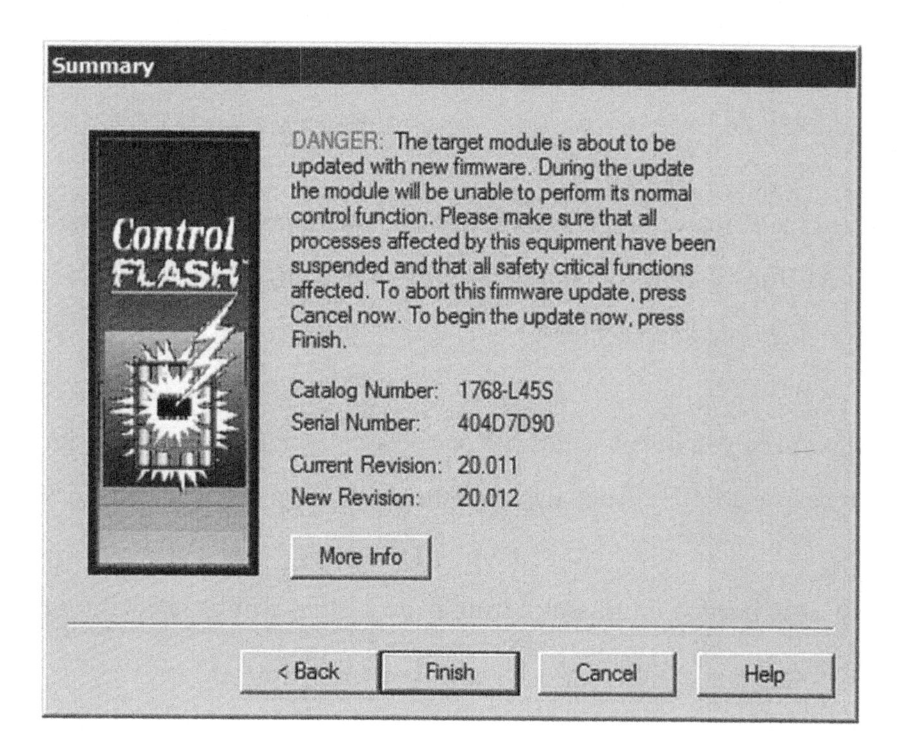

6. You can now download your Project ACD file to the new controller: Open your Studio 5000 or RSLogix 5000 project, connect via the communication tab and select the download option. Download should now proceed as normal.

Note on Step 1:

I first connected with a standard CP3 cable, which is the Allen Bradley null-modem cable, using the DF-1 (RS-232) driver, and then used the auto-configuration function in RSLinx. In this way, you can connect to the new processor in order to see the IP address setting of its EtherNet/IP port. You could then change either the IP address of the controller or the one on your laptop, in order to communicate via the Ethernet port. It is not recommended using the RS-232 serial port to update firmware.

Hands-On Exercise

1. Visit the Rockwell Automation website and obtain the latest version of Control FLASH for you PC or laptop. As of this writing ControlFlash v15 is available from the download center.

2. Make sure you have the desired or needed versions of firmware for the processor you'll update, also downloadable from the RA website.

3. Note the needed information from page 11 that will be needed for a firmware update.

4. If possible, setup a controller, perhaps a CompactLogix controller on your test bench, to practice the steps shown for updating firmware. Another option is to work with an existing ControlLogix or CompactLogix project as if you are needing to replace the Controller module with a new, out-of-the box module.

5. Follow the basic steps outlined on pages 12 - 13.

PROJECT ORGANIZATION:

Before getting into methods of addressing and creating tags for Studio 5000 programs, I want to spend some time looking into the important concept of Project Organization. It is a key to understanding many different elements of addressing, and how tags can be shared between different programs within the same project. Here are some basic definitions and examples related to Project Organization.

THE STUDIO 5000 PROJECT:

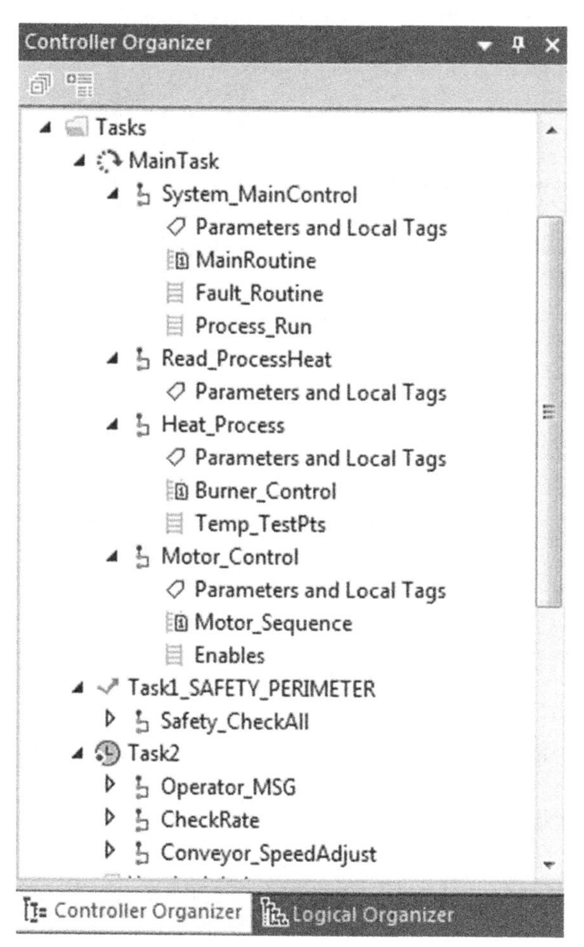

A project contains *all* the configured and programmed elements of the controller. It is composed of tasks, programs and routines, the tags used by those routines, and specialized tasks such as the Motion Planner, the Fault and Power-Up Handlers, and Safety if using GuardLogix redundant controllers. In other words, all the elements required for the programs to function are contained within the project. Here is an example of a project that I've named *Project GDA*, shown in a typical Studio 5000 application project organizer window. As you can see, much like a Window Explorer folder and file structure, a project is broken down into smaller and more defined sections which can be seen in the project illustration shown above. I've not been very descriptive in naming these sub-sections since the only purpose here is to show the basic relationships between a project and its associated *tasks*, *programs*, and *routines*.

Here is another way of looking into the basic organizational structure of a typical Studio 5000 project.

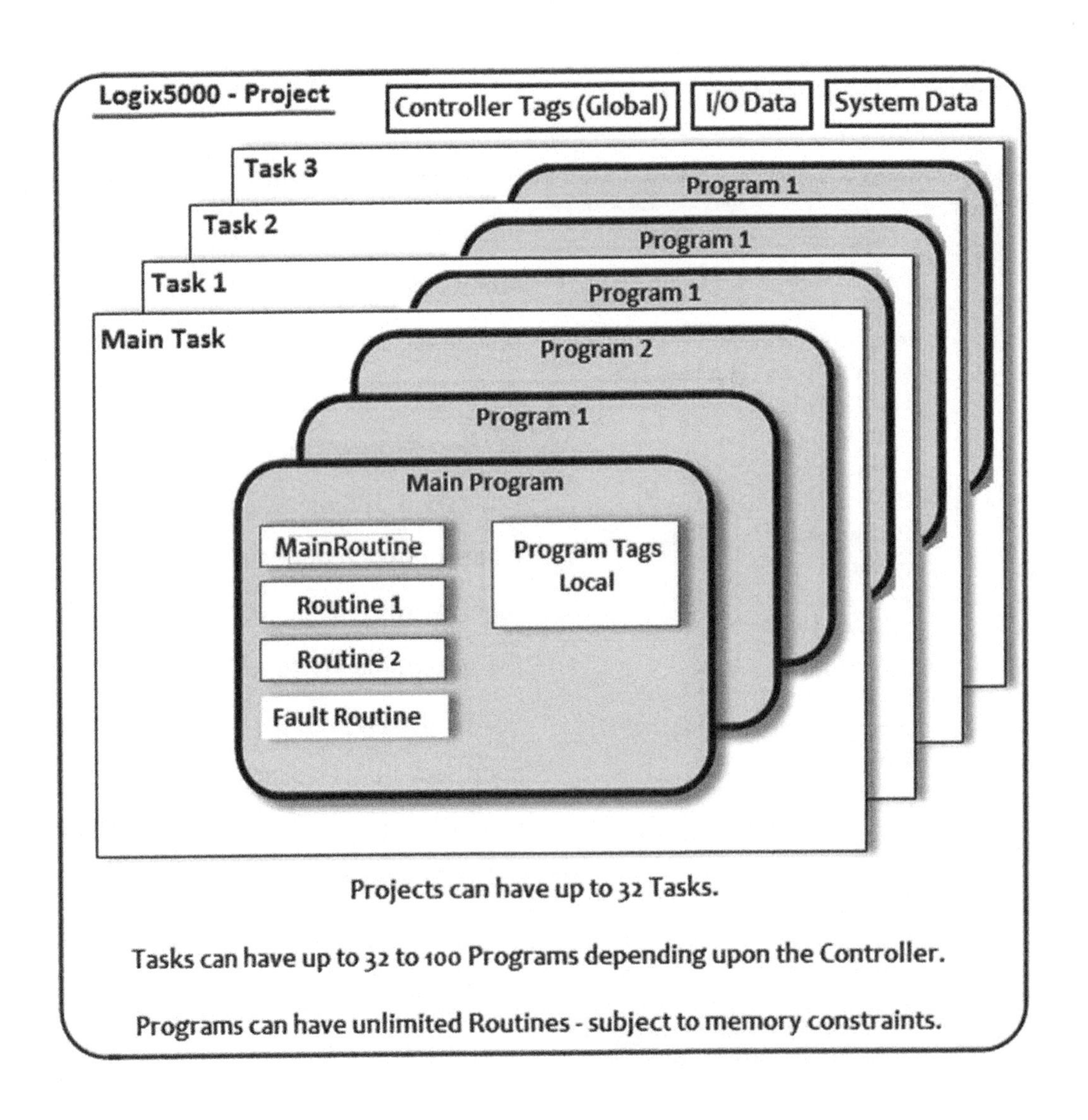

Once again, the project holds and organizes all the elements necessary for the control program to execute. In this illustration, note that some tags and data are *global* – meaning that the tags are available to all the programs in the project, while other tags and data are *local,* and available only to the routines within that specific program.

Let's look into the descriptions of the different components that are building blocks of a Studio 5000 project. As you can see, the major divisions are those pertaining to Tasks, Programs, and Routines – and we'll discuss each of these in that order.

TASK TYPES:

In the previous example shown, the Main Task is *continuous* with the others being *periodic* – denoted by the clock symbol on their folder icon in the project-tree. Each of these periodic tasks will start according to the time period (interval) that is set for the task, unless one with a higher priority is currently being executed. At this time interval the control exits the continuous task, executes the periodic and then returns to the continuous task, resuming in the place where it exited the routine. For this reason priority numbers, 1 through 15, are assigned to tasks. This allows a periodic task having a higher priority (lower number) to interrupt another periodic task that might be running during that time frame. The continuous task carries the lowest priority by default, and so will be interrupted by any periodic or event triggered tasks assigned to the project.

As shown in the previous illustration, a project can have up to 32 tasks – here I've shown only three, including the "Main Task", which is part of every project by default. Tasks fall into one of three categories, *continuous, periodic,* or *event triggered.* At least one task within the project *must be* designated as the "Continuous Task".

Studio 5000 and the ControlLogix platform support the use of multiple tasks in order to prioritize and schedule the execution of programs - based on specific events, timing or other criteria. It might be helpful to think of tasks by comparing them with SLC 500 program interrupts, such as sequenced timed interrupts, I/O interrupts, and event interrupts. While this is a somewhat crude comparison, just remember that project tasks are only an organizational tool or construct; which is used to determine the timing and sequencing of how program routines are executed.

CONFIGURING TASK TYPES:

The following shows how tasks can be designated as *Continuous, Event-triggered*, or *Periodic.* When a task is first created - or at any other time for that matter, you can bring up the *Task Properties* menu and select the drop-down menu for "Type" to designate the type of task you want. Other configurable items – such as event triggers and priority settings are set from this menu as well.

The following examples show an *Event* task which I've named "Safety_Perimeter", and also a *Periodic* task just named "Task2", that is set to trigger every 10 seconds. The same dropdown menu within the "Type" selection heading is where *Continuous* could be selected as well.

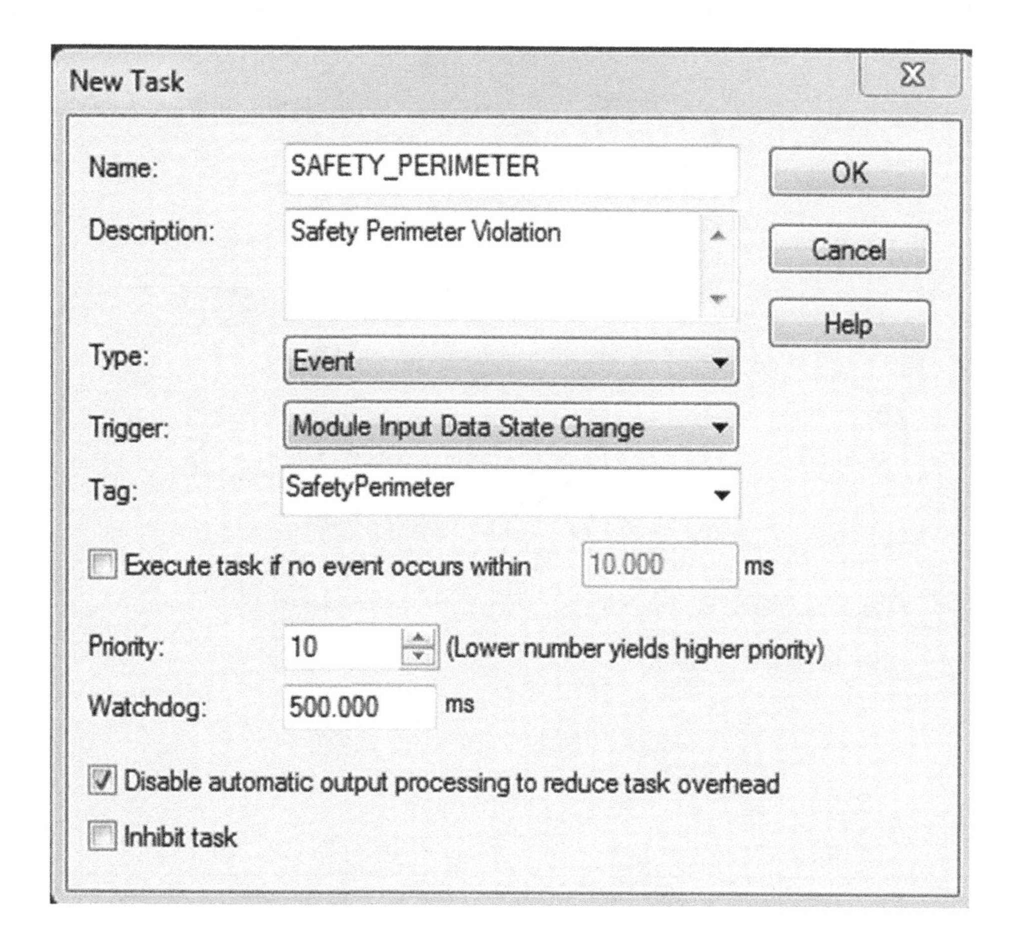

Some consideration must be taken for properly setting a value for the configurable watchdog timer. The general rule is to make sure all the programs/routines contained within the task have the time necessary to execute without exceeding the watchdog timer for the task – otherwise a major fault will occur. The task watchdog timer stops when all programs within the task have completed execution. You may also notice that when configuring an event-triggered task, that even in the absence of a triggering event, it can be executed as a periodic task if the "Execute Task If No Event Occurs Within" box is checked, and a time period entered. Here is the task property menu for periodic task.

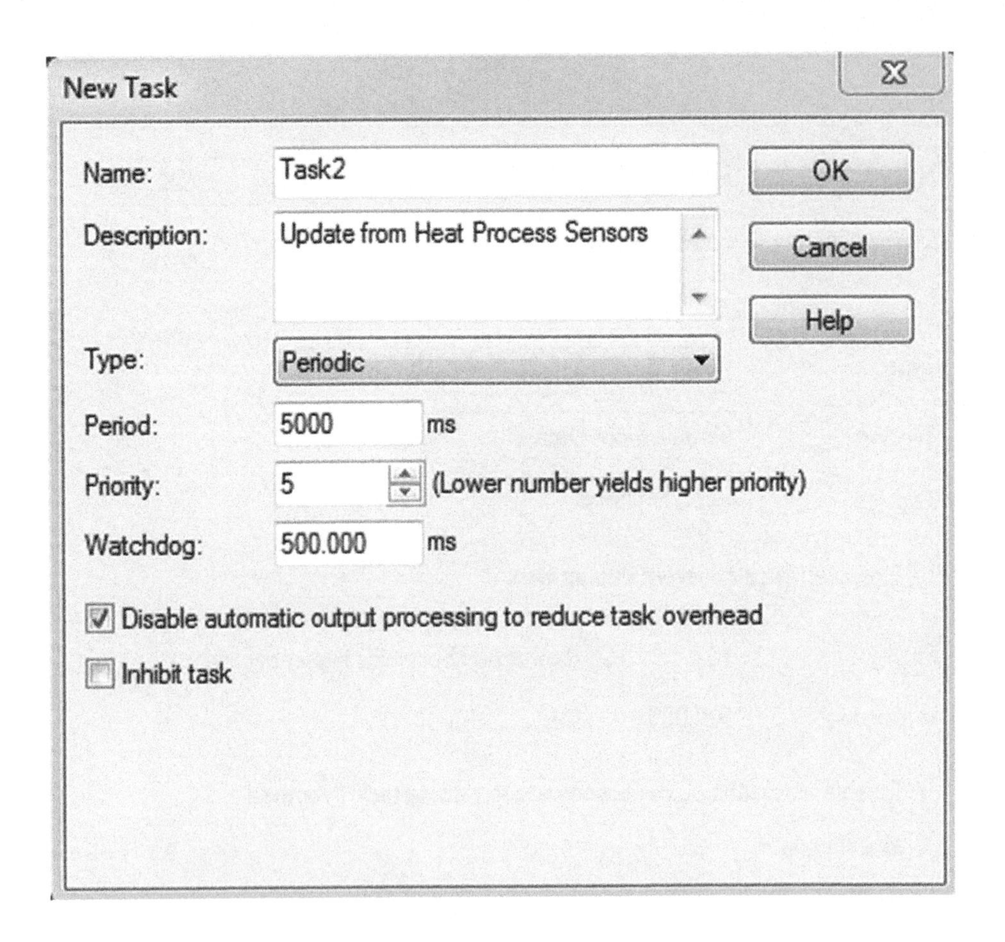

Even though many tasks can be created and used within a project, it's not always necessary or expedient to do so. Indeed, many projects will function entirely within a single continuous task. If a great many tasks are built into a project, time sequencing – even with event driven tasks, can present problems with task overlap – where tasks are constantly being interrupted and can't follow through to completion. On the other side of this issue, is the fact that the proper use of tasks can simplify coding, create logical program groupings, and create efficiencies in processor and memory use. So, when you consider the creation of additional tasks, it becomes important to ask a few questions:

- Could this code be executed within the continuous task as a separate program?

- Should this task be running in a continuous fashion or would periodic be more efficient?
- Should a given routine execute every 20 ms, 50 ms, or once every 5 minutes? What is the needed timing interval?
- Should the routine operate only when an external event is triggered?
- What priority should be assigned to the task? Should this task be interrupted, what would happen?

In addition to these main task types, here are some specialized tasks of which we need to be aware, and that operate in a different fashion than the ones just discussed.

- MOTION PLANNER / MOTION GROUP TASK: This is a specialized event task that, when triggered, starts immediately and interrupts all other tasks regardless of their priority. *Motion Planner* and its accompanying task are triggered when the event is set to trigger with the *Course Update Period* (CUP) setting in the task configuration menu. The event task, having a highest priority setting, will immediately execute after the Motion Planner. Course Update Period refers to the update interval of types of output modules that control axis movement.

- I/O TASK: This is a dedicated periodic task used by CompactLogix or FlexLogix controllers to process I/O data. This is not relevant to the ControlLogix controller. Note that this task doesn't show in the project-tree, but is automatically scheduled as a dedicated periodic task with a priority setting of "6". It then operates on the basis of the shortest "RPI" setting for system I/O modules. This task doesn't count toward the task limitation of the CompactLogix controller.

- <u>System Overhead Task</u>: This is *unscheduled communication* that is not configured through normal I/O channels. The "System Overhead" task only interrupts the continuous task.

Programs & Routines:

Within the scheduled intervals of periodic, event-triggered and continuous tasks, the next item most directly affecting the sequence of program execution, is simply the *order in which programs are listed.* Tasks can hold multiple programs, as in this example, and those programs will execute in their listed order. In the following illustration, I've renamed the Task 2 programs with more descriptive names - you can do this by doing a right-click on the program name and selecting properties. By right-clicking on the Task and displaying the Task Properties dialog menu, you can select the <u>*Program Schedule*</u> tab, should you want to move one program ahead of another. In this example, you might want to move the <u>Operator MSG</u> program ahead of the <u>CheckRate</u> and <u>ConveyorSpeed</u> programs.

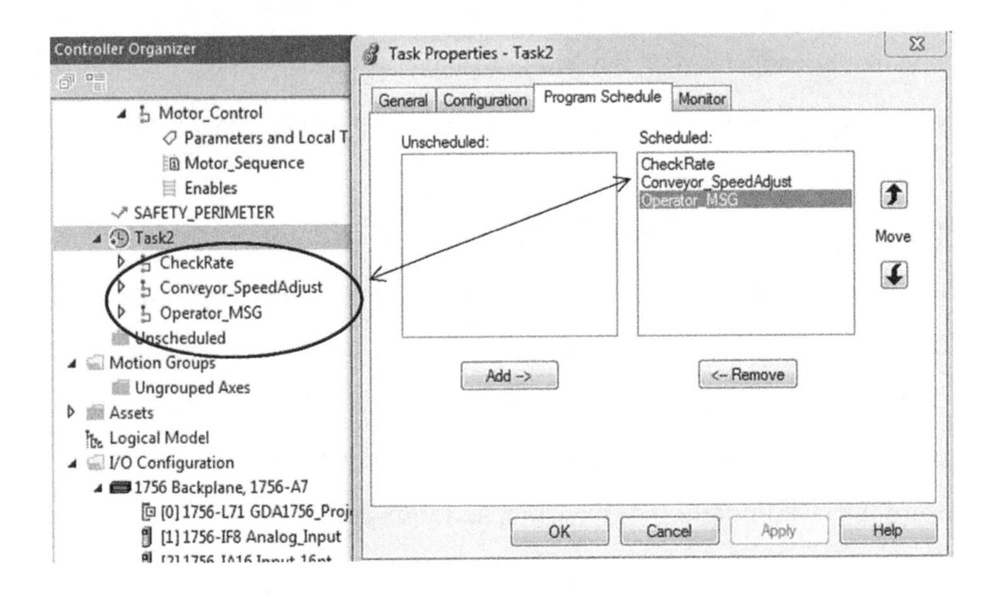

ROUTINES:

The routines of a program are composed of the programming code that will be executed by the controller. Every program must contain a designated *Main Routine*. This *Main Routine* logic will execute first and direct when other sub-routines run, by the use of program flow instructions - such as the *jump-to-subroutine* (JSR) instruction. In other words, routines within the program are ignored unless they are called by a JSR from the *Main Routine*. Of course, other periodic tasks may interrupt the program execution and routine at any point, given timing constraints and higher priority settings. In which case, program execution would return to the exited routine once the higher priority task has completed. In the example that follows, you can see that I've changed the names of several programs and routines. This is done by doing a right-click on the program and selecting *Program Properties*. From the General Tab you can rename a program or add a description, and from the Configuration Tab you select which routine will act as the *Main Routine* of that particular program.

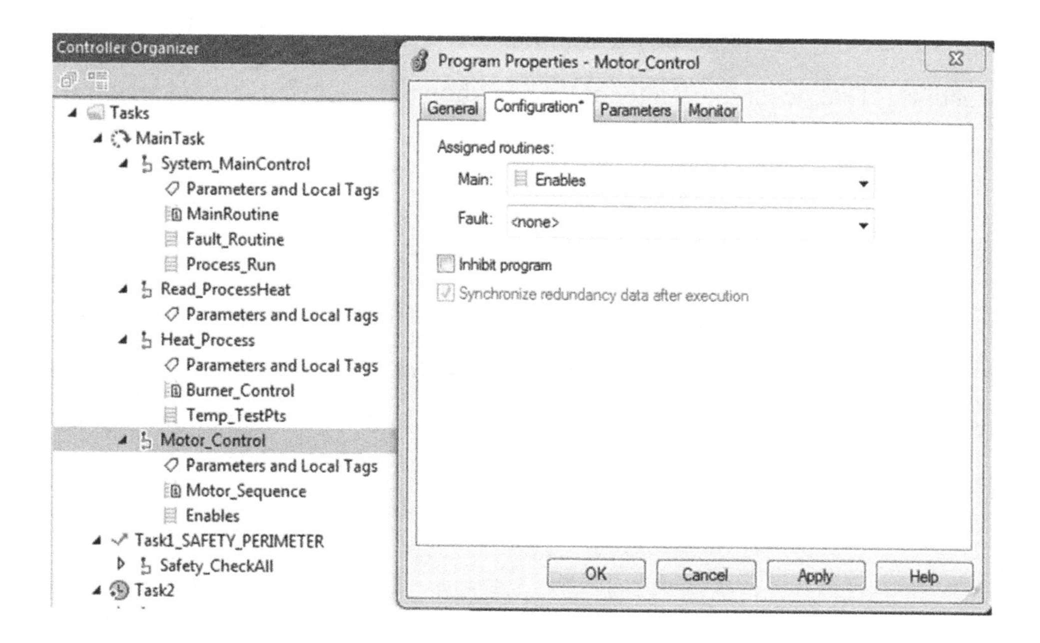

On each main routine, there is a small *page symbol* with the number 1, which indicates this routine is the selected main routine for the program. A main routine doesn't require the title of *MainRoutine* and can be renamed with terms that correspond more directly with the functions of the program. As you can see from the example, in the *Heat_Process* program, *Burner_Control* is designated as the main routine. In the *System_MainControl* program, *Motor_Sequence* is currently designated as the main routine; but here we can make a change and designate the *Enables* routine as the new main routine.

Remember that any given routine allows only *one type* of programming. Structured Text (ST) programming, which is well suited for scenarios where math equations or other types of calculations are needed, must be programmed into its own dedicated routine. The same holds true for Functional Block Diagrams (FBD) and Sequential Function Chart (SFC) programming.

A program can hold a large number of routines, with some controllers able to hold up to 65,535 routines. I've never encountered that and hope I never do – but understand it can be done.

My view on how things should be done, especially when programming controls, always leans toward keeping things clean and simple. Of course; a routine doesn't have to be long and cumbersome. The use of multiple routines *can* make programs easier to follow, step-through, and troubleshoot - if the routines are created with some thoughtfulness and good planning.

Summary for Project Organization

- Projects can hold up to 32 tasks for ControlLogix and *most* CompactLogix controllers.
- The Controller will process one task at a time.
- Tasks are the mechanism used to provide *timing and sequencing* for program execution.
- All tasks have a watchdog timer with a default of 500 ms. This can be set from 1 to 2 million ms.
- The time-period set for a periodic task must allow enough time for its programs to run.
- There are other types of periodic specialty tasks, *Motion Planner, I/O*, and *System Overhead.*
- Each task can hold up to 32 programs. In some cases, up to 100 depending on the controller.
- Within a task, only one program at a time is executed - in the order they are listed.
- Placement (order) of a program within a task allows the controller to know when to run the program, and provides logical grouping for the routines and data.
- Each program must have a designated *Main Routine* and utilize instructions such as the JSR to execute other sub-routines within the program.
- Programs can hold up to 65,535 routines depending on the controller.
- Routines are comprised of the actual programming code.
- Routines can be programmed using Ladder logic, Functional Block Diagram (FBD), Sequential Function Chart (SFC) or Structured Text (ST) programming.

- In each routine – only one type of coding is allowed.
- See Rockwell Automation Pub 1756-PM005D for additional information on CompactLogix family of controllers.

HANDS-ON EXERCISE

1. Create at least two additional TASKS; one a periodic task, and another an event triggered task.

2. Create two or three programs within each of your created tasks.
   a. Name these programs.
   b. Change the order of execution of programs within a task.

3. Create routines within Tasks:
   a. Create routines within the Main Programs of the different Tasks – that can be called by JSR's within the Main Routine.
   b. In Main Routine – create ladders using JSR instructions, to call other routines within the program.

I/O MODULES:

The I/O modules in a ControlLogix or CompactLogix system, just like conventional PLC's, provide the link between the logic program and the physical conditions of the machinery or processes we want to control. Those conditions may simply be the on/off state of a remote switch or pushbutton, the position of a part on a moving conveyor, or the temperature of parts undergoing a heat-treating process. All field devices; switches, light or ultrasonic sensors, thermocouples or RTD's require connections to specific modules which can translate their voltage or current signals into a digital signal the controller can process.

Here is an illustration of the terms and characteristics that compose a module's catalog ID, along with many of the characteristics typically seen in a ControlLogix project.

What's in a Catalog ID?

Bulletin	Function	Voltage Range	No. Points or Channels	Unique Characteristics
1756 ControlLogix 1769 CompactLogix 1768 CompactLogix	Input (I) Output (O) Communication Remote I/O Specialty	A: 79-132 VAC B: 10-30 VDC C: 30-60 VDC F: Analog (V or I) G: TTL rated H: 90-146 VDC M: 159-265 VAC N: 10-30 VAC R: RTD T: Thermocouple V: 10-30 sourcing	Input or Outputs Points or Channels	D: Diagnostics I: Isolated Inputs/Outputs E: Electronically Fused F: Fast Peer Control H: HART

The ControlLogix modules – Bulletin 1756, fall into five general categories: Digital, Analog, Specialty, Communication, and Controller. These modules are all software configurable, alleviating the need to change dip-switches and jumper blocks on certain types of modules. In general, features for ControlLogix and CompactLogix modules include:

- The use of removable terminal blocks (RTB), or interface wiring modules (IFM)
- Integral time-stamping capabilities
- On-board diagnostics
- Electronic keying
- The ability for removal and insertion (RIUP) under power. Note however that RIUP is not an option with CompactLogix systems since they are din-rail mounted and connect into adjoining modules.

Digital Modules:

These types of modules essentially provide an "on" or "off" state to the controller's logic program, and also a means of sending a voltage out to turn on remote devices such as relays, solenoids or status indicators. Additional important functions provided by a digital module is input filtering – which can prevent false active states, and optical isolation between incoming voltages and the controller. These modules vary by the voltage and current ranges they can support, the number of input or output points they have, the type of output provided – such as relay or triac outputs, and whether they are "sinking" or "sourcing" types of modules. Here are several examples:

- 1756-IA16: 16 point input module (AC)
- 1756-IA8D: 8 point diagnostic input module (AC)
- 1756-IA16I: 16 point isolated input module (AC)
- 1756-IB16: 16 point input module (DC)
- 1756-OA8E: 8 point output module / electronically fused (AC)
- 1756-OB16D: 16 point diagnostic output module (DC)
- 1769-IA16: 16 point input module (AC) for CompactLogix controller

As you can see from these few examples, each module – whether an input or output module, has unique features that are designated by its alpha-numeric identifiers. As shown in the previous illustration, the first four digits of the module denote the bulletin number, 1756 for a ControlLogix controller and 1768 or 1769 for a CompactLogix controllers. Next is the function type which designates an input or output module, a communications module, or a module that serves as a bridge to remote I/O. What follows the function are letters that designate at what voltages or current level the module is rated. At the end of this string of characters, is a numeric value denoting the number of terminal points or channels. One final letter listed, is one which designates unique capabilities for the module, these might include "I" for isolated input, "D" for diagnostic capabilities such as fault latching and time-stamping, or the letter "G" for a TTL input module. Reference Rockwell Publication 1756-UM058D-EN-P for full descriptions and wiring specifications for digital modules.

Analog Modules:

Analog modules provide a variable current or voltage input to the controller, or output to field devices. Common examples of analog signals are a 4 to 20 mA current signal, a 0 to 10 vdc, or a -10 to +10 vdc variable voltage signal. Also widely used are specialty devices that sense flow, temperatures, perform high-speed counting applications, and intelligent devices that update their status and report back to the main controller via high-speed network connections. In this section however, we'll mainly look into the more traditional style of analog modules and basic configurations.

Here are several different analog modules – both input and output types. Like any Allen Bradley module, special consideration and attention must be given to the catalog number with the unique identifiers it contains, in order to build a project that accomplishes the desired control.

- 1756-IF8: 8 point non-isolating analog current / voltage input
- 1756-IF16: 16 point non-isolating analog current / voltage input
- 1756-IF6CIS: 6 point sourcing, current-loop input
- 1756-IR6I: 6 point isolated RTD input
- 1756-IT6I: 6 point isolated Thermocouple/mV input
- 1756-OF8: 8 point non-isolated current / voltage output
- 1756-OFCI: analog current output
- 1769-IF8: 8 point non-isolating analog current / voltage input (CompactLogix)
- 1769-IT6: 6 point Thermocouple/ mV input (CompactLogix)
- 1756-IF8H &1756-OF8H: HART modules are hybrid analog modules designed to provide an interface for HART remote devices. These are capable of transmitting diagnostic or status information by superimposing a digital signal upon the 4 to 20mA analog signal.

Other design features typical for ControlLogix analog modules is the ability for individual channel configuration, auto-calibration features, selectable filters and power sources, selection between single-ended or differential inputs, and the ability to detect input values that are over or under range.

Refer to Rockwell Publication 1756-UM009 for specifications and types of analog modules that can be used in a ControlLogix or CompactLogix project.

Specialty I/O Modules:

These are, just as the name implies, modules designed for very specialized functions. Examples of the tasks assigned to these modules are duties such as reading flow-meter signals, high-speed counter applications, or ASCII and Modbus device interfacing. Here are examples of these module types:

- 1756-CFM: Flowmeter module – can read magnetic pick-up from flow turbine
- 1769-SM2: Modbus Interface / PowerFlex Drive
- 1756-HSC: High Speed Counter
- 1769-HSC: High Speed Counter (CompactLogix)
- 1769-ASCII: ASCII device interface for RS-232, RS-485 and RS-422

Communication Modules:

These modules serve to provide network connections between a controller and local or remote I/O, connections for messaging, and connections for produced and consumed tags. A *produced* and *consumed* tag is the name given to data that is shared between different controllers within a given network. One controller is the producer of the data, and multicasts that data per the configured RPI of the consumer controller. It is not sent dependent upon program logic within either of the controllers, but rather the RPI setting (information request) - of the consumer controller. More will be discussed on these tag types in chapter 4, including a more detailed set-up for communication modules.

Here is a listing of several of the types of modules commonly used to establish bridge connections which extend the scale and reach of a given control network. For a more complete and descriptive list see Rockwell Automation PUB 1756-TD0031.

- 1756-EN2F: EtherNet/IP Bridges
- 1756-EN2T
- 1756-EN2TR
- 1756-EN3TR: ControlNet Bridge
- 1756-DHRIO: DeviceNet Bridge for Remote I/O
- 1756-ENBT: Data Highway Remote I/O

CONTROLLER MODULES:

Since the ControlLogix platform allows for multiple processors on a single chassis, we can also consider a controller as a module. Note that while the ControlLogix architecture allows for multiple processors to be installed within the same rack or chassis, the CompactLogix processor does not. It is din rail mounted and connected module-to-module (CompactLogix 1769-L3), or a processor with embedded I/O – such as the CompactLogix 1769-L23. Even though it doesn't support having multiple processors on the same rail, it is possible to communicate with another processor assembly using the communication module options for the CompactLogix system.

For full specifications on different controllers refer to the Rockwell PUB 1756-TD001 found on their online library.

1756-L8X CONTROLLERS:

This latest generation of ControlLogix controllers, the L8's, boast impressive performance in terms of capacity and data throughput. User-memory ranges from 3MB for the L81 to 40MB for the L85. In addition, the L8 group can handle up to 300 Ethernet/IP nodes, 128K digital and 4K analog maximum I/O points, and 32 tasks with up to 1000 programs per task.

1756-L7x Controllers:

The 1756-L7x series controllers: the -L71 through –L75, have an impressive track record as well. The main difference in these controllers is the amount of user memory available. The L71 has 2MB of user memory and each subsequent model doubles that amount – thus the –L75 has 32 MB of user memory. The L7 series can accommodate a maximum of 500 network connections, utilizes a capacitive energy storage module rather than a battery, and has a USB port available for PC connection or firmware revisions.

1756-L6x Controllers:

These earlier controllers, -L61, L62, L63, L64 and L65, have the same amounts of user memory available: 2, 4, 8, 16, or 32 MB. They differ in that they handle a maximum of 250 network connections, have a serial port (9-pin) connection, and utilize battery backup of volatile memory rather than the capacitive energy storage modules utilized on the L7's.

1756 – GuardLogix Controllers:

These are controllers that operate in tandem with another controller – essentially a dual controller solution that satisfies the requirements for SIL 3 integrity compliance. SIL 3 is a safety integrity level defined by the IEC 61508 standard. This will often be shown in conjunction with a *performance level* rating, such as "PL*(x)*", which indicates the probability of the dangerous failure of equipment or a process. To meet these safety requirements; 1756-L7's are paired with another controller - a 1756-L7SP (safety partner) module and 1756-L6 controllers are paired with a 1756-LSP controller module. These safety partners, provide redundant controller capabilities in the handling of safety related tasks, and when set to a SIL 3 level, the logic they scan and execute cannot be modified. The main controller, L7 or L6 continues to operate as any other standard controller in allowing online editing, and the ability to enable and use forces, while the safety partner controller maintains monitoring and execution of the integral safety tasks, programs and logic.

Configuration of Modules:

As we start this section on configuring modules, some of the first things to understand are the common features they share, and some of the common terms associated with I/O and Controller modules. Then we'll look at several step-by-step examples of module configuration. Let's begin with these concepts that are considered common features:

- RIUP – In a ControlLogix system, this acronym means the module is able to be *removed or_inserted under power*. This is not an available feature with the CompactLogix 1769 rack, which is din-rail mounted and connects module-to-module rather than through a back-plane.

- Fault Reporting – gives both hardware and software indications when there is a problem with a module.

- Software Configurable – Configure each module upon installation as each module is added to the project or return later to a module to edit settings or values, or to retrieve fault diagnostic information.

- ELECTRONIC KEYING – this is a safety mechanism designed to protect against the installation of a module that is incompatible or non-functional according to the design of your project. Selections for *Electronic Keying* are as follows:

    1. to allow compatible modules,
    2. to allow only an exact match,
    3. to disable electronic keying for the module
    4. Note: if exact match is set, then a comparison is done on vendor, device type, product code, and the major and minor revisions of the module to those defined in the project.

COMMON FUNCTIONS & TERMS

- OWNERSHIP – Every module in a control system must be owned by a controller. This owner controller performs several functions and have these characteristics:

    - Stores configuration data for the module.
    - Sends the module its configuration data.
    - Maintains & monitors its communication connection with the module.
    - The owner / controller and module relationship can be local or remote.
    - Input modules can have more than one owner.
    - Output modules can have only one owner.

- PRODUCER / CONSUMER – A network model that allows for the interchange of data between controllers, modules and various system devices. While some devices produce data to be shared, other devices are consumers (receivers) only.

- RPI – *Requested Packet Interval* – is the time interval the controller/CPU uses to request current data from the module.

- RTS – *Real-Time Sampling* – if set, the RTS defines the time interval, with which the module will scan its inputs for new data, store the sampled data and send it to the controller/CPU.

- MODULE INHIBIT – inhibits functioning of a module without requiring its actual removal from the project or chassis.

- MAJOR FAULT ON CONNECTION FAILURE – creates a major fault on the processor should a module fail.

- ARCHIVING – is an input scanning function used in high-speed analog modules whereby the module stores data input samples of each channel in its internal buffers before multicasting data to the controller.

SAMPLE PROJECT I/O CONFIGURATION:

Here again is the project tree (Controller Organizer) for a sample project. I've created an I/O configuration containing some different modules to show as examples, a 16 point - 120 VAC input module, a 24 VDC output module, and an analog input module. Later we'll add, or at least show the configuration, of a thermocouple module and a specialty module.

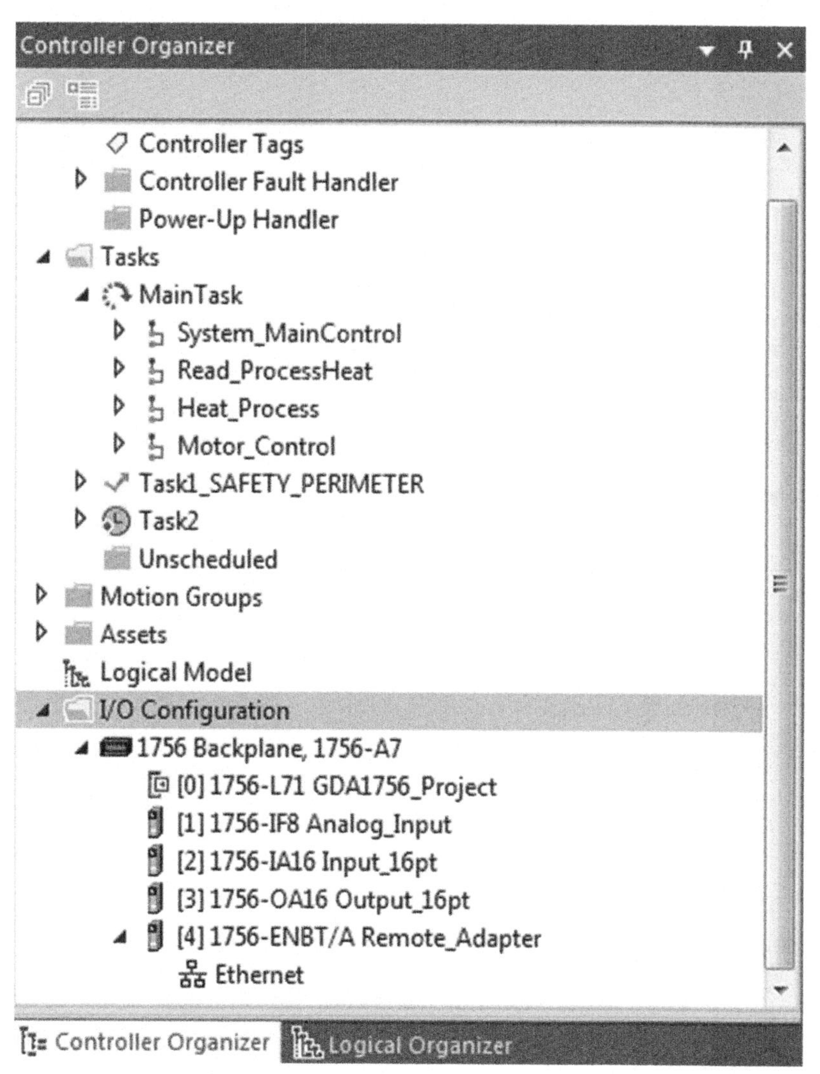

Analog Module Configuration:

Recall that to add modules to your project, you follow these basic steps. A right-click on the I/O Configuration folder; allows the selection of a new module, and brings up the following menu. In this case, I'll add an additional 1756-IF8 voltage/current analog module and designate its location as slot 5.

1756-IF8 Module:

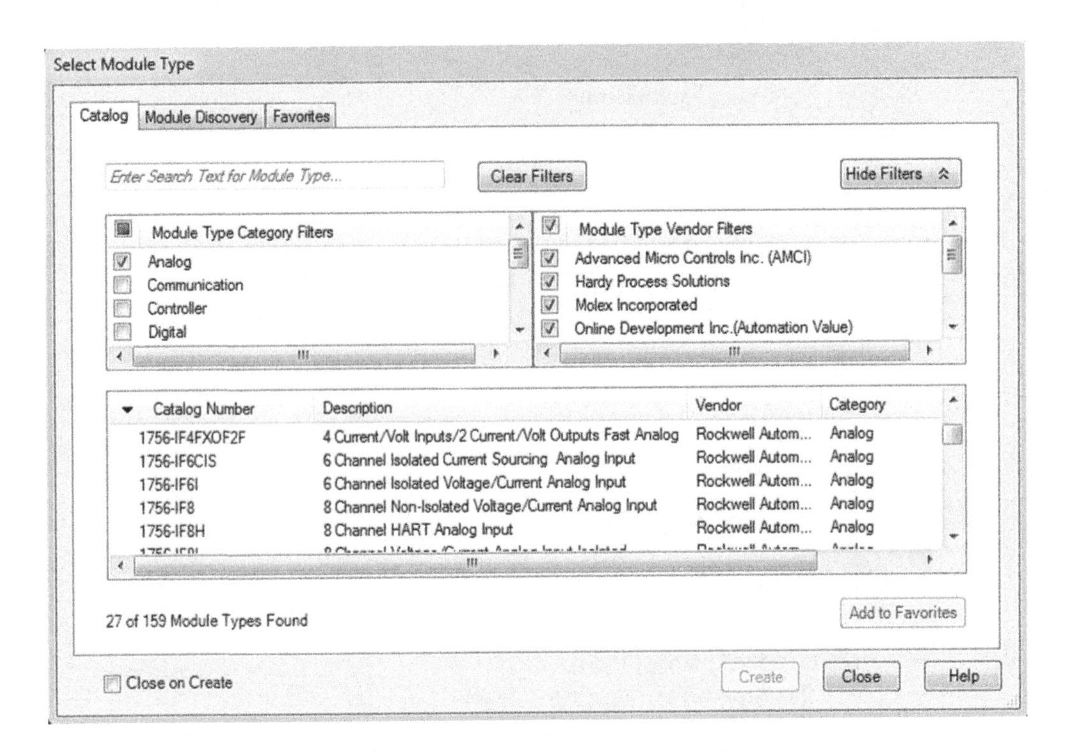

Once the module is selected and you click on the "Create" button, you see the following menu screen. From this "New Module" screen, you can *name* the module, *add a description,* and *assign it to a slot* location.

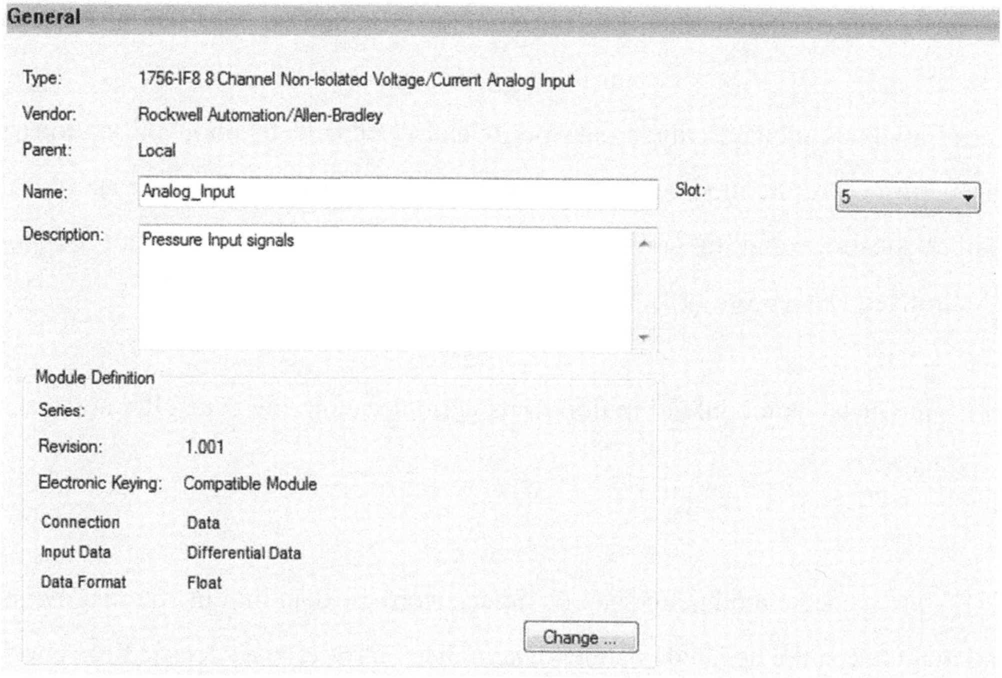

General

Type: 1756-IF8 8 Channel Non-Isolated Voltage/Current Analog Input

Vendor: Rockwell Automation/Allen-Bradley

Parent: Local

Name: Analog_Input   Slot: 5

Description: Pressure Input signals

Module Definition

Series:

Revision: 1.001

Electronic Keying: Compatible Module

Connection Data

Input Data Differential Data

Data Format Float

Change ...

It is also from this menu, that configuration begins for the analog module and each of its 8 channels. From the General menu tab, you see that I've given the module a short name and description, and designated slot 5 as its location.

On this same menu you will see the *Change* button which allows editing to be accomplished to some of the module's basic features – such as the electronic keying feature. As you can see, I've chosen to allow the *Compatible Module* electronic keying option for this particular module.

Under the *Connection* tab, the following menu appears, allowing you options to set an RPI value for the module, to inhibit the module from functioning, and to determine what should occur if the module loses communication with the controller.

When configuring analog modules it is important to remember the following:

- These modules multicast their data periodically, dependent upon the options you configure, where the module resides within the control system – such as a local or remote location, and to some extent the type of network protocol employed (ControlNet, DeviceNet, or EtherNet/IP).

- RPI – instructs the module to multicast its current data to the controller at a specific time interval.

- RTS – instructs the module to scan its inputs, store the data into its internal memory, and to multicast the updated channel data to the controller at a specific time interval.

In this example I've left the RPI setting at 20 ms, and set the controller to allow a major fault condition if it and the module lose their connection.

Connection

Name	Requested Packet Interval (RPI) (ms)
StandardInput	20.0 0.2 - 750.0

☐ Inhibit Module

☒ Major Fault On Controller If Connection Fails While in Run Mode

One detail of which to be aware, when setting RPI values, is the scenario of having I/O modules that are located in a remote chassis. If communication is over a CIP type of network – such as ControlNet, the limiting factor for RPI is the *network update time* (NUT) of the network. A network, such as ControlNet, polls all network nodes for data. Therefore the RPI for remote modules can't be set for update times that are faster than the update time of the network. For projects where I/O modules are installed within a local chassis this is not a problem, and RPI can usually be selected within the full range for the module.

Next, click on the Configuration tab to view the area where we'll actually configure individual channels for either current or voltage, a range selection for the (V) or (I), choices for filtering the input signals, and finally the data format selections for the data used within the program logic. Here are some selections made for channel 3:

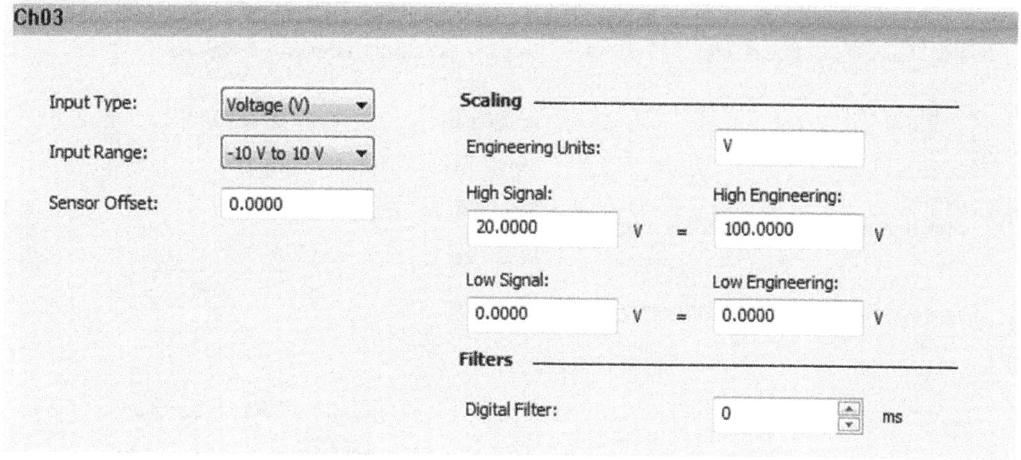

Ch03

Input Type: Voltage (V)
Input Range: -10 V to 10 V
Sensor Offset: 0.0000

Scaling
Engineering Units: V
High Signal: 20.0000 V = High Engineering: 100.0000 V
Low Signal: 0.0000 V = Low Engineering: 0.0000 V

Filters
Digital Filter: 0 ms

Remember that RTS is the rate at which the module will read these channels, store the data in its memory, and then send that data to the controller; while the RPI controls only the time interval the module uses to send or multicast the current data it has in its memory to the controller. Therefore, if RTS is set to a time-rate faster (less than) than the RPI, then the controller will receive data from the module at the RTS rate. If the RTS is set at a rate slower (greater than) the RPI, then data is multicast at both the RPI and RTS intervals – but only the RTS multicast contains updated input data.

1756-IT6 Module:

Another type of analog input card, a thermocouple module, and its basic configuration is shown in the following example. When you look at the module properties menu, you see the different options unique to this module, and that require configuration settings. On various tabs, selections can be make for the data format, thermocouple type, the type of units, filtering, and selecting how the control module should respond if it detects an open circuit between it and the field device.

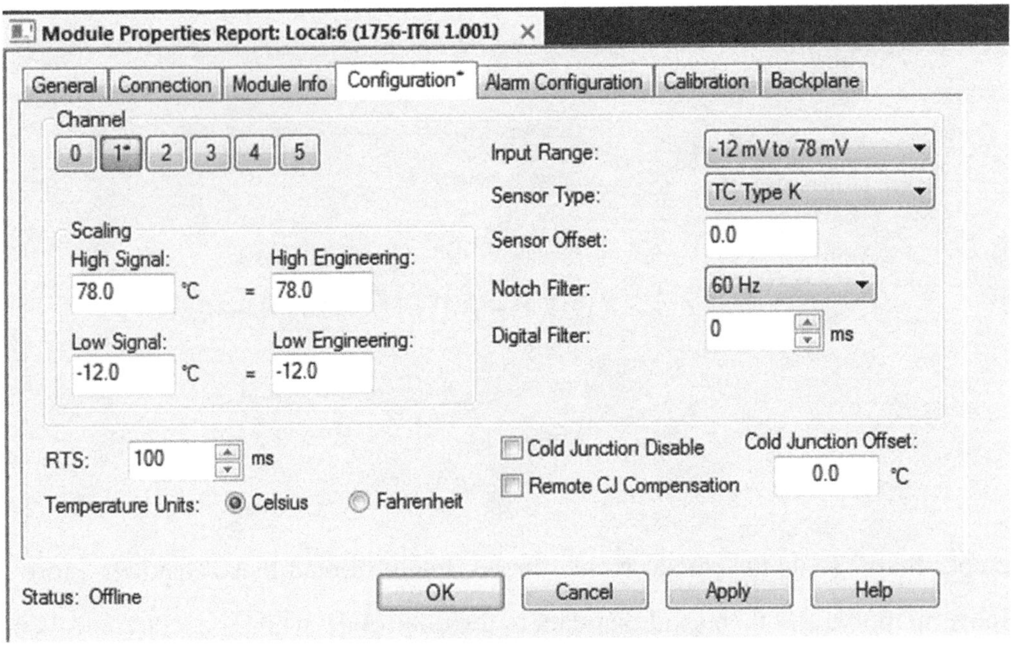

Module Properties Report: Local:6 (1756-IT6I 1.001)
General | Connection | Module Info | Configuration* | Alarm Configuration | Calibration | Backplane
Channel: 0 1* 2 3 4 5
Input Range: -12 mV to 78 mV
Sensor Type: TC Type K
Sensor Offset: 0.0
Notch Filter: 60 Hz
Digital Filter: 0 ms
Scaling
High Signal: 78.0 °C = High Engineering: 78.0
Low Signal: -12.0 °C = Low Engineering: -12.0
RTS: 100 ms
Temperature Units: Celsius Fahrenheit
Cold Junction Disable
Remote CJ Compensation
Cold Junction Offset: 0.0 °C
Status: Offline
OK Cancel Apply Help

Digital Module Configuration:

Digital modules are relatively easy to configure – keeping in mind those features already mentioned that are common and pertain to all ControlLogix or CompactLogix modules. As you can see from these example illustrations – some of the main configuration details for a digital module – whether an input or output, are the same as would be configured for any of the modules just discussed.

1756-IA16 Module:

After creating the module in I/O Configuration > double-click the module to enter the *Module Properties* menu, where you can then give the module a name, a description, and assign it to a slot position.

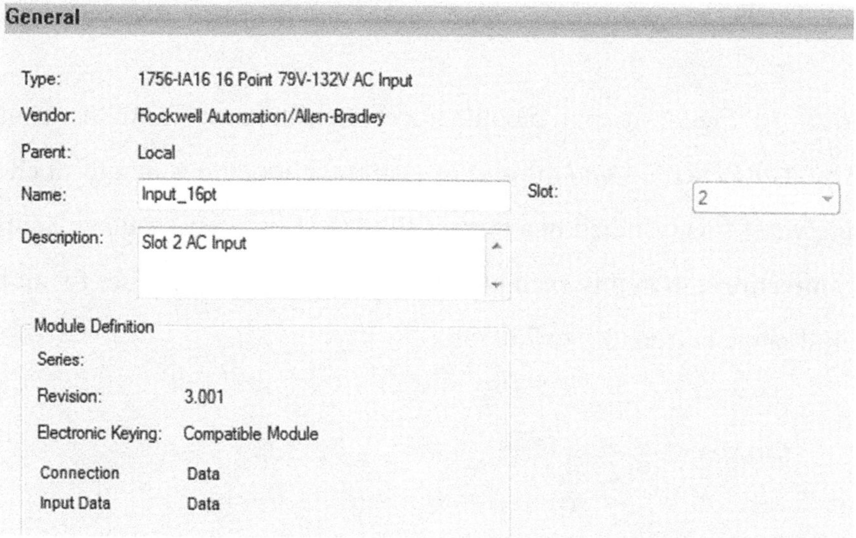

General

Type: 1756-IA16 16 Point 79V-132V AC Input
Vendor: Rockwell Automation/Allen-Bradley
Parent: Local
Name: Input_16pt
Slot: 2
Description: Slot 2 AC Input

Module Definition
Series:
Revision: 3.001
Electronic Keying: Compatible Module
Connection: Data
Input Data: Data

Within the "Module Definition" menu that you can change or edit the series, revision, the electronic keying, and select the type of connection and data format for the module.

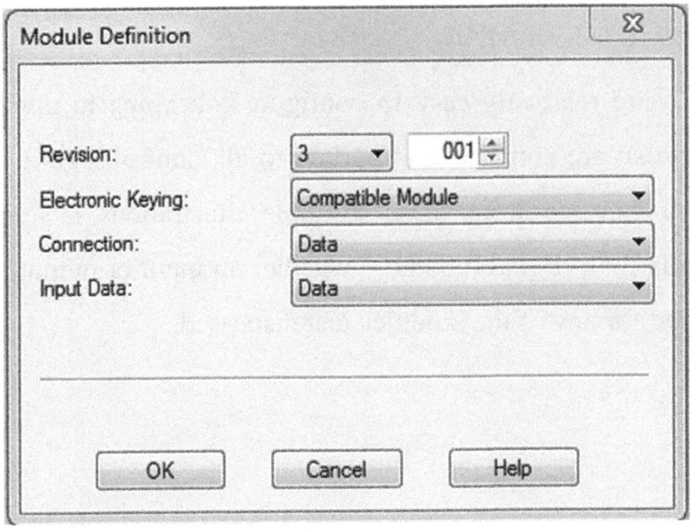

Module Definition

Revision: 3 001

Electronic Keying: Compatible Module

Connection: Data

Input Data: Data

OK Cancel Help

Digital input modules always multicast their data to the controller at the RPI interval configured, and also at the change-of-state (COS) rate - if enabled. If COS is enabled for the digital input module, it multicasts its inputs upon the occurrence of a transition change in input states.

By comparison, a digital output module receives data sent from the controller as determined by its RPI setting *and* the end-of-task if the module is in a local chassis; and at its RPI interval if it is installed in a remote chassis. Looking at the module properties menu and **connection tab** in this example, we see that the module is set for an RPI of 20 ms, but the full range is from 0.2 to 750 ms.

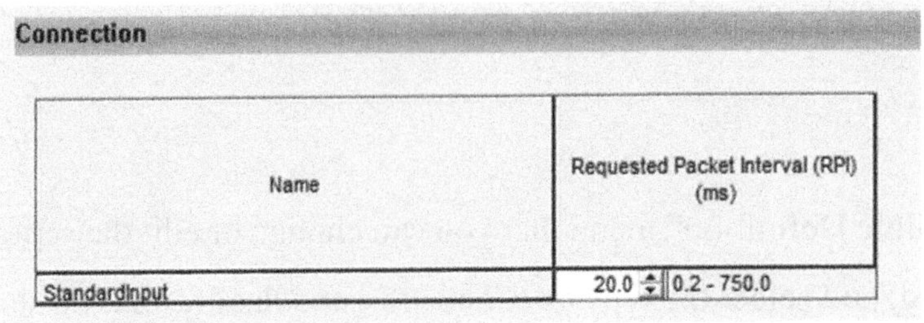

Connection

Name	Requested Packet Interval (RPI) (ms)
StandardInput	20.0 0.2 - 750.0

Here is an example of a ControlLogix 1756-IA16 input module, with the *Configuration Tab* selected. Here we can apply filtering options to a *range* of input points.

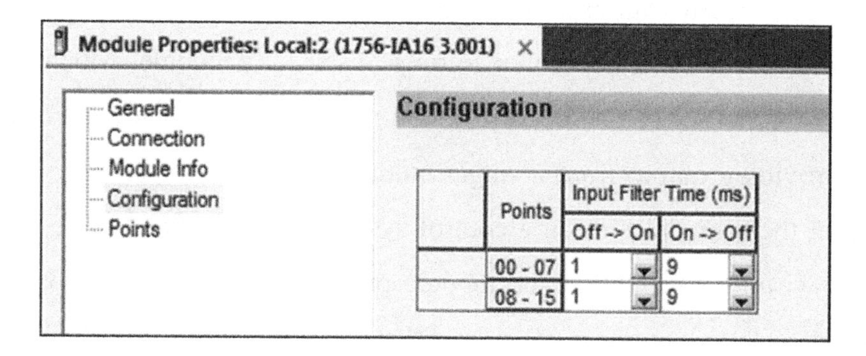

In the following example; when the *Points* property tab is selected, it's possible to enable and use individual points, for *on-to-off* and *off-to-on* transitions, or change-of-state (COS).

Module Properties: Local:2 (1756-IA16 3.001)

- General
- Connection
- Module Info
- Configuration
- Points

Points

Point	Enable Change of State	
	Off->On	On->Off
00	✓	✓
01	✓	✓
02	✓	✓
03	✓	✓
04	✓	✓
05	✓	✓
06	✓	✓
07	✓	✓
08	✓	✓
09	✓	✓
10	✓	✓
11	✓	✓
12	✓	✓
13	✓	✓
14	✓	✓
15	✓	✓

Specialty & Communication Module Configuration:

What should be very evident by now, is that all modules must be configured, and that each module is designed with characteristics unique to the module. No other module types exemplify this more clearly than the group of specialty modules which, much like those used in SLC 500 or PLC-5 platforms, combine the duties of both receiving input signals and providing output from a single module. Because of the very specialized nature of what these modules do in a control system, it is expedient to be thoroughly familiar with wiring and usage of the module prior to installation and configuration. There are many selections to be made during the setup of these modules - so here are a few basic examples of configuration menus on several specialty modules.

1756-HSC Module:

This module is used for high-speed counting applications such as axis positioning or velocity feedback. After adding the module (*I/O Configuration > New Module*) - we enter the *Module Properties* menu:

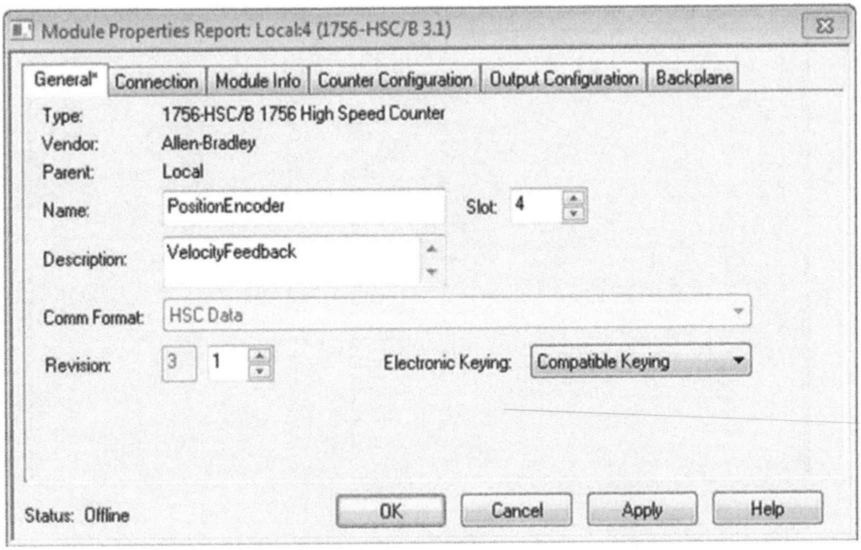

Module Properties Report: Local:4 (1756-HSC/B 3.1)
General* | Connection | Module Info | Counter Configuration | Output Configuration | Backplane
Type: 1756-HSC/B 1756 High Speed Counter
Vendor: Allen-Bradley
Parent: Local
Name: PositionEncoder
Slot: 4
Description: VelocityFeedback
Comm Format: HSC Data
Revision: 3 1
Electronic Keying: Compatible Keying
Status: Offline
OK Cancel Apply Help

From this initial menu we can give our new module a name, a description, assign it to a slot, change the revision number, and enable or edit our electronic keying options. As you will notice, there are several more configuration tabs available to select for setting up different options for this module.

Here are additional tabs for the Connection, Counter Configuration and Output Configuration options.

Connection Tab: This is where you would set the RPI for the module. Also two important checkboxes: one that if checked, allows a *major fault* if the connection fails between the module and the processor (communication with the controller); and another checkbox that allows you to inhibit the module – even through it is installed in the rack. This last checkbox, the inhibit, can be helpful when testing or troubleshooting the different module options:

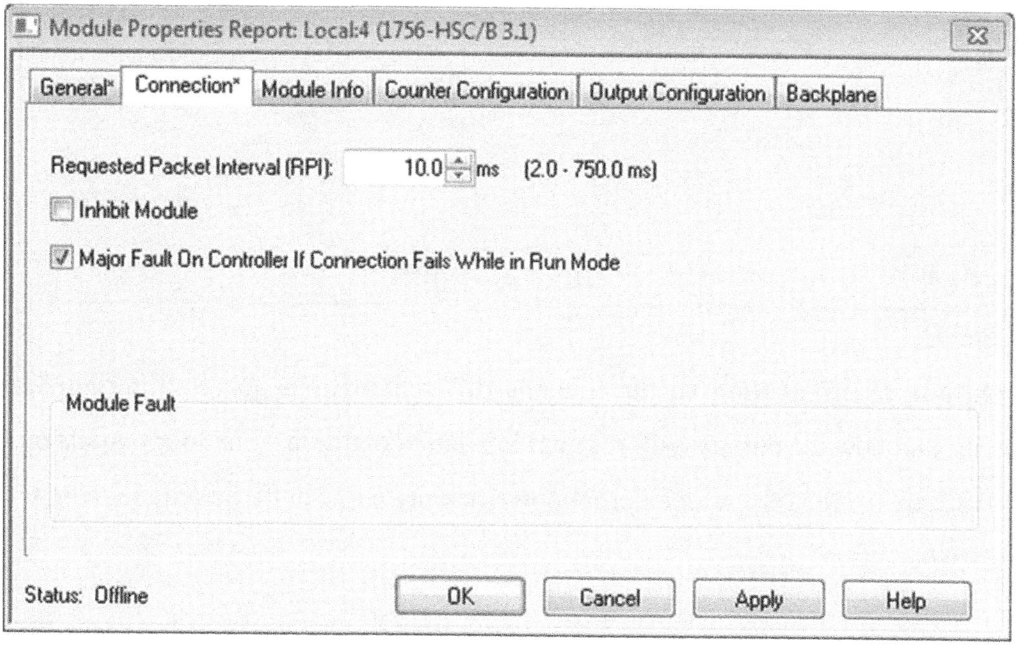

Module Properties Report: Local:4 (1756-HSC/B 3.1)

General* | Connection* | Module Info | Counter Configuration | Output Configuration | Backplane

Requested Packet Interval (RPI): 10.0 ms (2.0 - 750.0 ms)

Inhibit Module

Major Fault On Controller If Connection Fails While in Run Mode

Module Fault

Status: Offline

OK | Cancel | Apply | Help

The **Counter Configuration Tab** is used to define how you want the module to handle the input counts from a field device. These modules can be used in counter mode, as shown in the following example, or in a frequency mode. Counter mode selections would accommodate inputs from encoders or pulse generators. Frequency mode is used in applications where feedback for rate measurement is required.

As you go through the drop-down menus there are other selections for storage modes, preset values, and filters.

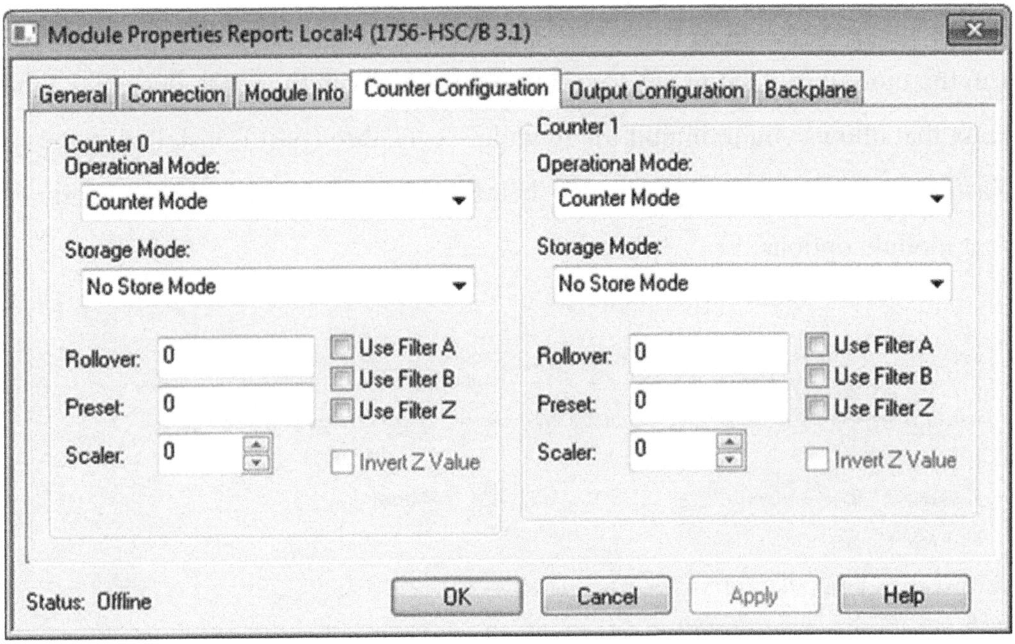

Module Properties Report: Local:4 (1756-HSC/B 3.1)

General | Connection | Module Info | Counter Configuration | Output Configuration | Backplane

Counter 0
Operational Mode: Counter Mode
Storage Mode: No Store Mode
Rollover: 0
Preset: 0
Scaler: 0
Use Filter A
Use Filter B
Use Filter Z
Invert Z Value

Counter 1
Operational Mode: Counter Mode
Storage Mode: No Store Mode
Rollover: 0
Preset: 0
Scaler: 0
Use Filter A
Use Filter B
Use Filter Z
Invert Z Value

Status: Offline
OK | Cancel | Apply | Help

The **Output Configuration** menu contains different options for configuring output terminals, and how the outputs will respond in a fault condition. The four outputs on the 1756-HSC are sourced from an external power supply and can be linked to a counter or frequency operation.

Each of these can be configured to turn on and off at specified accumulated values of the selected counter. These onboard outputs operate independently of the controller scan cycle.

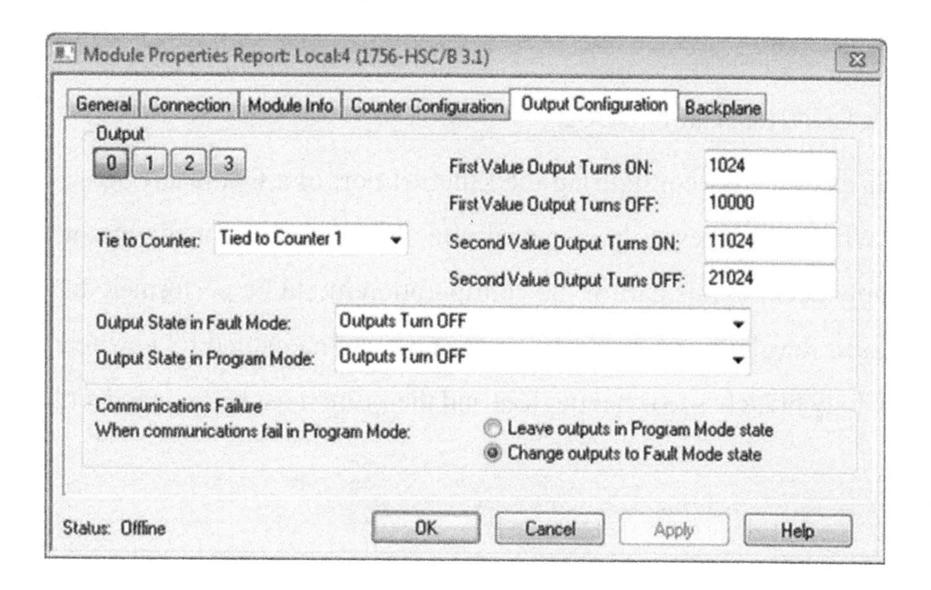

1756-ENBT Module:

Here is an example of a communication module configuration menu for the 1756-ENBT module used in a typical ControlLogix system.

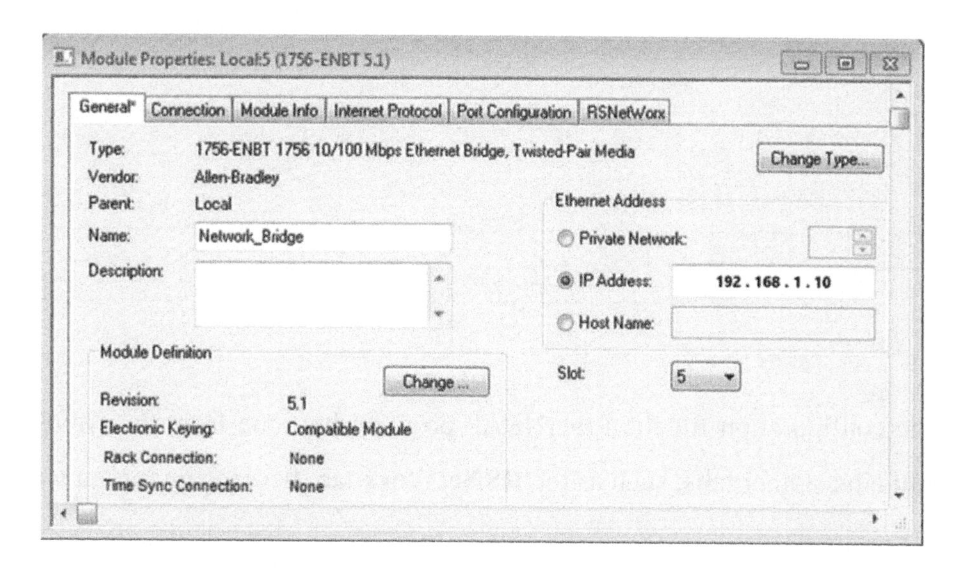

Much like the EtherNet/IP port on a new processor, the ENBT module will require a valid IP address within the overall network, and provides for communication with other devices on the same network, such as an HMI, VFD drives, remote I/O, or another controller.

1769-L35E Controller Module:

Here is an example for configuring the Ethernet port of a CompactLogix 1769-L32E processor. While not necessarily a specialty module, I thought it important to at least mention simply because this part of the configuration might be performed during a later phase of project development. This processor port can be cabled to a switch where the network topology branches to other devices and therefore must be assigned an IP address.

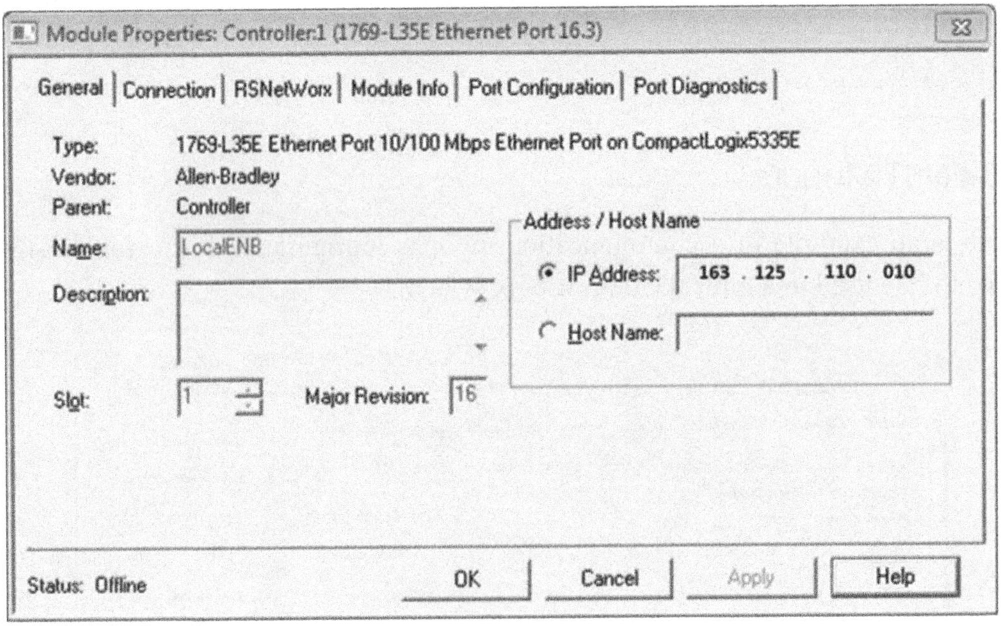

Module Properties: Controller:1 (1769-L35E Ethernet Port 16.3)

General | Connection | RSNetWorx | Module Info | Port Configuration | Port Diagnostics

Type: 1769-L35E Ethernet Port 10/100 Mbps Ethernet Port on CompactLogix5335E
Vendor: Allen-Bradley
Parent: Controller
Name: LocalENB
Description:
Slot: 1 Major Revision: 16

Address / Host Name
IP Address: 163 . 125 . 110 . 010
Host Name:

Status: Offline
OK Cancel Apply Help

Most of the configuration for the EtherNet/IP port can be done from the **General** and **Connection** tabs. Other tabs, such as the **RSNetWorx** tab, become important whenever setting up a network with remote I/O. For example, a ControlNet network – where data requests are scheduled for different devices on the network. The RSNetWorx application is also available for configuring EtherNet/IP and DeviceNet networks.

Key Concepts: I/O Modules & Configuration

- I/O Modules provide links between program logic and physical conditions and operations.

- In the Logix 5000 platform, I/O modules are *Software Configurable*.

- There are five general categories of modules: Digital, Analog, Specialty, Communication, and Controller modules.

- ControlLogix supports RIUP or removal and insertion under power.

- CompactLogix does not support RIUP.

- Modules provide Fault Reporting capabilities and indications.

- Modules allow for *Electronic Keying* to prevent the installation of an incompatible module.

- Ownership – Every module is *owned* by a controller. This controller stores the configured data for the module, verifies and maintains the communication connection with the module.

- Input modules can have more than one owner.

- Output modules can have only one owner.

- Producer / Consumer – refers to a network model that allows the interchange of data between controllers and other system devices. Modules, as well as Controllers, can be a producer or consumer of data.

- RPI – *Requested Packet Interval* – the time interval configured in a module to transmit its data to the controller (input module), or receive data from the controller (output module).

- RTS – *Real-Time Sampling* – defines the time interval an input module uses to scan its inputs for new data and send data to the controller. (Analog Input Module)

- COS – *Change-of-State* – used by digital inputs as a trigger to send data to the controller. This can be more efficient for the controller since it is only receiving new data when inputs have changed.

- Module Inhibit – the configuration setting that allows you to disable (inhibit) the functioning of a module without requiring its removal from the project.

- Archiving - an input scanning function used with high-speed analog modules where samples are taken over a programmed time period and stored into the internal memory of the module before being sent to the controller.

HANDS-ON EXERCISE

Create a new project similar to that shown in the previous sections – you might use the example shown on page 37.

In sections that follow there will be opportunities for addressing, tag creation, designating tag types, building user-defined data types and basic routines – all of which can be integrated into this example project.

Here are some suggested things to do:

1. Create a new project with controller, either ControlLogix or CompactLogix, and at least three modules.

2. Add the modules to configuration:
    a. An – IA16 digital input module.
    b. An – OB16 output module.
    c. An – IT6 thermocouple module.

3. Configure each module with a basic configuration. Once again, the goal is to gain familiarity with these processes, menu options, and general procedures.

I/O Address Structures & Tag Creation:

Studio 5000 addressing and tag creation, is one of the most important topics we'll consider, and often one of the most confusing. That being the case, let's first look into the type of addressing related to some of the I/O modules discussed in the previous chapter. Remember earlier, I made the statement that when we selected and configured a module for a project- that Studio 5000 *automatically* creates a group of tags – tags that are unique to that module. These tags are placed within the *Controller Tags* folder of the Controller Organizer or project-tree.

If I install a 1756-IA8D module, (note the letter "D"), Studio 5000 creates addressing (base tags) for the eight input points - and also for the diagnostic data which can be used in program logic or passed along as produced data to another controller. This will be more clearly seen in examples that follow, and we'll take a careful look at the components that make-up the basic address structure. By doing a double-click on *Controller Tags* at the upper portion of the Organizer, you bring up the following screen which shows all the installed I/O modules, their *base* addresses, values, and data types.

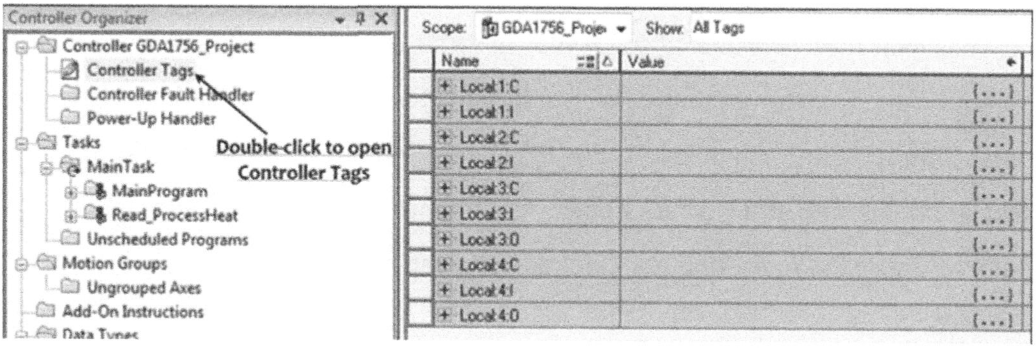

When viewing the Controller Tags > Monitor Tab, you see the addressing for the installed modules, slots 1 through 4, in the monitor pane on the right side of the application. Each of these modules have defined data structures, designated by single letters, for different elements within their design. These can be further expanded to fully see their data and values. To do this, simply click on the plus (+) symbol allowing the module structure to expand, and the basic components of I/O addressing are more clearly seen. Here is an illustration with brief descriptions for these structural elements.

Five components of an I/O Address

Location : Slot : Type . Member. Property or Bit

Location	Slot	Type	Member	Property or Bit
Local or Remote (adapter or bridge)	Slot where module is assigned	Input (I) Output (O) Config (C) Status (S)	Specific Member data component- unique to module: examples Ch6Data Ch6Config Fault	Specific Property or Bit related to the Member: examples specific channel or point number or name Property or Bit may not always be used

When you open the *Controller Tags* folder and the *Monitor* screen, you see that this information has already populated the address fields for each module added to the example project. Notice that the 1756-IF8 analog module assigned to slot 1, shows nomenclature for **Local: 1: I** and **Local: 1: C** - meaning that there are analog *input* channels, and also *configuration data* elements for the module.

The address components tell us that this module resides in the *local* chassis – rather than being remote and communicating through an adapter bridge, it also shows the *slot assignment for the module* and *the type of data* (I and C) that the module holds.

If you consider this, it really isn't too different from what we were accustomed to seeing in SLC-500 and PLC-5 programming, although the syntax order was slightly different. In that style of addressing structure it is common to use the type designation first: O, I, S2, B3, T4, C5, R6, N7, and F8. If we needed an additional integer file we could add a new 255 word file and call it N11 or N12. The address always included the slot where a module was assigned, and also indicated whether we were referencing a word, a terminal point, or single bit – by the use of delimiters within the address structure. Therefore we would see addressing which looked like this:

- **I:1/3** references input module in slot 1, terminal point 3
- **O:2/5** references output module in slot 2, terminal point 5
- **B3:5/11** references the binary file, word element 5, bit 11
- **N7:50** references the integer file, word element 50 (all 16 bits)

In the ControlLogix platform, *Location* is the first item included as part of the address structure, perhaps because of the fact that these controllers are often used in larger scale control topologies with remote controllers, remote I/O and bridge adapters. Much like the older PLC nomenclature, *Slot* and *Type* are included, although the listed types are different and fall within only four general categories: Input (I), Output (O), Configuration (C), and Status (S). Reasons for this will become clear as we look at the next illustrations which further define these categories by *tag type, data type,* and *style.*

In the following example, the address structure has been expanded, and now shows configuration data, high/low ranges, and alarm latches for **Ch0Config** of this module. Here is an example with an overlay of the alarm configuration menu we used earlier – just so you can see – this was where configuration values were being stored during initial module configuration or set-up.

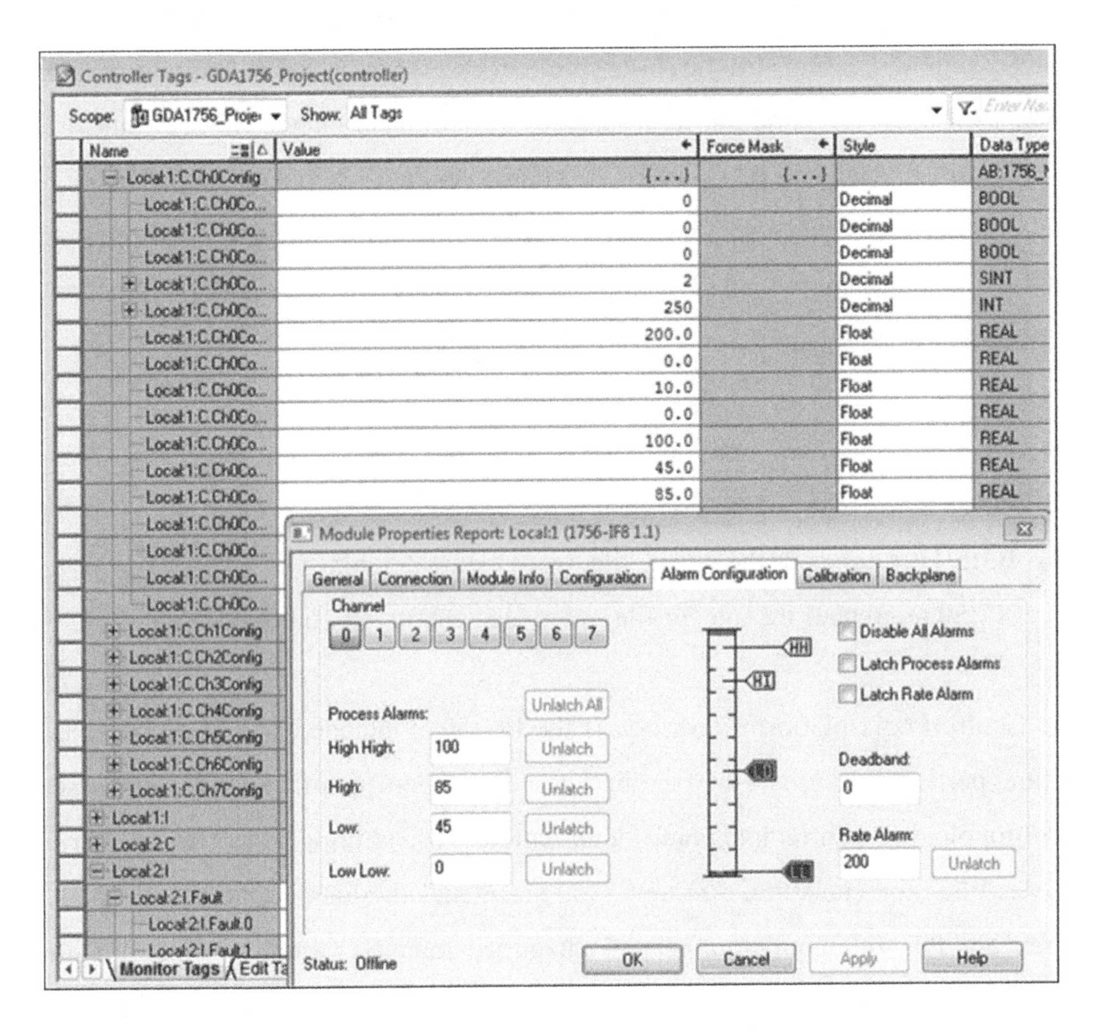

The **Ch0Config** term is the *member* of the address structure. This is similar to a designated *word* in the addressing syntax for the SLC-500. If you recall, there are instances where you must designate the word and then the specific bit number – such as our example B3:3/14 (bit 14 of word 3 of the B3 file). At other times it is only necessary to address to the word level – N7:50 (word 50 of the N7 file). So while the *member* term is similar – it isn't exactly the same either.

In Studio 5000, the member term can be a predefined name or "tag", as in these instances: *Ch1Config, Ch2Data,* or *Fault2*. I use the term, predefined, because they are not names which I had to invent and enter – all I did was install the module and do basic configuration. In the Rockwell literature, these are also referred to as a *structured data type* because it is a predefined structure that can combine several different data types.

In the following example, **Local: 1:C.Ch0Config**, contains elements or sub-members that include several data types including BOOL, SINT, INT, and REAL.

Controller Tags - GDA1756_Project(controller)

cope: GDA1756_Proje Show: All Tags

Name	Value	Force Mask	Style	Data Type
− Local:1:C	{...}	{...}		AB:1756_IF8_Flo...
+ Local:1:C.ModuleFilter	2		Decimal	SINT
+ Local:1:C.RealTimeSample	100		Decimal	INT
− Local:1:C.Ch0Config	{...}	{...}		AB:1756_NII_Str...
Local:1:C.Ch0Config.Alar...	0		Decimal	BOOL
Local:1:C.Ch0Config.Pro...	0		Decimal	BOOL
Local:1:C.Ch0Config.Rat...	0		Decimal	BOOL
+ Local:1:C.Ch0Config.Ra...	2		Decimal	SINT
+ Local:1:C.Ch0Config.Digi...	0		Decimal	INT
Local:1:C.Ch0Config.Rat...	0.0		Float	REAL
Local:1:C.Ch0Config.Lo...	0.0		Float	REAL
Local:1:C.Ch0Config.Hig...	10.0		Float	REAL
Local:1:C.Ch0Config.Lo...	0.0		Float	REAL
Local:1:C.Ch0Config.Hig...	100.0		Float	REAL
Local:1:C.Ch0Config.LAl...	-10.0		Float	REAL
Local:1:C.Ch0Config.HAl...	10.0		Float	REAL
Local:1:C.Ch0Config.LL...	-10.0		Float	REAL
Local:1:C.Ch0Config.HH...	10.0		Float	REAL
Local:1:C.Ch0Config.Alar...	0.0		Float	REAL
Local:1:C.Ch0Config.Cal...	0.0		Float	REAL

After the *member* term is established, a sub-member (*property* or *bit*) can be designated. The following example shows the address structure fully expanded to show all elements of the address syntax – including property names and bits where applicable.

Expanded to show:
Location:Slot:Type.Member.Property

⊟ Local:1:C.Ch0Config	{...}	{...}		AB:1756_NI_Str...
Local:1:C.Ch0Config.AlarmDisable	0		Decimal	BOOL
Local:1:C.Ch0Config.ProcessAlarmLatch	0		Decimal	BOOL
Local:1:C.Ch0Config.RateAlarmLatch	0		Decimal	BOOL
⊟ Local:1:C.Ch0Config.RangeType	2		Decimal	SINT
Local:1:C.Ch0Config.RangeType.0	0		Decimal	BOOL
Local:1:C.Ch0Config.RangeType.1	1		Decimal	BOOL
Local:1:C.Ch0Config.RangeType.2	0		Decimal	BOOL
Local:1:C.Ch0Config.RangeType.3	0		Decimal	BOOL
Local:1:C.Ch0Config.RangeType.4	0		Decimal	BOOL
Local:1:C.Ch0Config.RangeType.5	0		Decimal	BOOL
Local:1:C.Ch0Config.RangeType.6	0		Decimal	BOOL
Local:1:C.Ch0Config.RangeType.7	0		Decimal	BOOL

As you can see, the member *Ch0Config* has a property *RangeType* which, according to its Data Type of *SINT*, designates eight bits 0-7. Each individual bit has a Data Type designation of BOOL. Note that with Studio 5000, each address is allowed up to 32 bits for its stored value, but what it actually uses is designated by the *Data Type* value, either predefined or user-defined, which can be BOOL (1 bit), SINT (8 bits), INT (16 bits), DINT (32 bits), or REAL (32 bits).

DATA TYPES & ALLOCATED MEMORY:

Since we're talking about Data Types, this may be a good time to show the following chart showing details about each of the Data Types typically used with Studio 5000 programming and the ControlLogix platform. Also introduced is a bit of information about the *Structured Data Types* used for Timers, Counters, PID's, and so forth. You recall that in the SLC-500 platform, the Timer instruction had 16 bit words assigned as part of their *control structure* for the *Preset* and *Accumulator* values, and assigned control bits for the *timer timing* (TT), *enable* (EN) and the *done* (DN) bit.

These are also the items included within the address structure in the ControlLogix system, and like the analog address tags previously shown, can be seen from the *Monitor Tags* or *Tag Editor* menu.

RSLogix Data Types

Data Types:	Bits Used:	Values Possible:
BOOL	Bit 0	0 or 1
SINT	Bits 0 - 7	-128 to 127
INT	Bits 0 - 15	-32,768 to 32,767
DINT	Bits 0 - 31	-2,147,483,648 to 2,147,483,647
REAL	Bits 0 - 31	Floating Point Negative -3.40282347E38 to -1.17549435E-38 Positive 1.17549435E-38 to 3.40282347E38

Additional Structured Data Types

Data Type:	Stored Data:
Timer:	Timer Instruction control structure
Counter:	Counter Instruction control structure
Control:	Array Instruction control structure
Message:	MSG Instruction control structure
PID:	PID Instruction control structure

Structured Data Type for a Timer

- Part_CycleTime	{...}	{...}		TIMER
+ Part_CycleTime.PRE	0		Decimal	DINT
+ Part_CycleTime.ACC	0		Decimal	DINT
Part_CycleTime.EN	0		Decimal	BOOL
Part_CycleTime.TT	0		Decimal	BOOL
Part_CycleTime.DN	0		Decimal	BOOL

If the (+) symbol beside the PRE or ACC control words is clicked-on, they expand to show the full 32 bits of the DINT by which they are defined. Of course there isn't much need to do that since you can see their value in decimal form in the adjoining field, but note that they are allotted 32 bits (DINT) rather than the 16 bit allocations we used with the SLC-500 family of controllers.

Next, let's move to the digital input module created in our project - located in slot 2 – and discuss some of the attributes of the input points or channels shown. In this slot we assigned a 1756-IA16 digital input module which will receive input voltage signals from field devices – such as pushbuttons, limit switches, pressure switches, or door-safety sensors – any number of things that only need to send back a discrete signal, so the logic program knows its status - *on* or *off*. Because of this, each point or terminal will need to be addressed down to a *sub-member – bit level* syntax – much like the illustration above (page 60), where *RangeType* was expanded to show its component individual bits; *RangeType.0, RangeType.1*.... through *RangeType.7*, and each assigned a BOOL Data Type.

Scope: GDA1756_Proje Show: All Tags

Name	Value	Force Mask	Style	Data Type
+ Local:1:C	{...}	{...}		AB:1756_IF8_Flc
+ Local:1:I	{...}	{...}		AB:1756_IF8_Flc
+ Local:2:C	{...}	{...}		AB:1756_DI:C:0
− Local:2:I	{...}	{...}		AB:1756_DI:I:0
+ Local:2:I.Fault	2#0000_00...		Binary	DINT
− Local:2:I.Data	2#0000_00...		Binary	DINT
Local:2:I.Data.0	0		Decimal	BOOL
Local:2:I.Data.1	0		Decimal	BOOL
Local:2:I.Data.2	0		Decimal	BOOL
Local:2:I.Data.3	0		Decimal	BOOL
Local:2:I.Data.4	0		Decimal	BOOL
Local:2:I.Data.5	0		Decimal	BOOL
Local:2:I.Data.6	0		Decimal	BOOL
Local:2:I.Data.7	0		Decimal	BOOL
Local:2:I.Data.8	0		Decimal	BOOL
Local:2:I.Data.9	0		Decimal	BOOL
Local:2:I.Data.10	0		Decimal	BOOL
Local:2:I.Data.11	0		Decimal	BOOL
Local:2:I.Data.12	0		Decimal	BOOL
Local:2:I.Data.13	0		Decimal	BOOL
Local:2:I.Data.14	0		Decimal	BOOL
Local:2:I.Data.15	0		Decimal	BOOL

In this example, I've expanded the **data member** of the module address that shows the actual input terminal points, but as you can see, there is also an address structure for the (C) configuration data. This holds the configuration values we assigned earlier that pertains to filtering and enabling change-of-state settings (COS) for input points.

Looking at the *Local:2:I.Data* address that is open, you will also see its default *Data Type* of DINT. This acronym means, as you can see in the previous chart, that it assigns a *double integer* in memory, or 32 bits, for this data. Of course this module only has 16 terminal points, and if you open up the COS configuration screen, you would see only the first 16 bits (0 through 15) enabled for reporting to the controller their change-of-state.

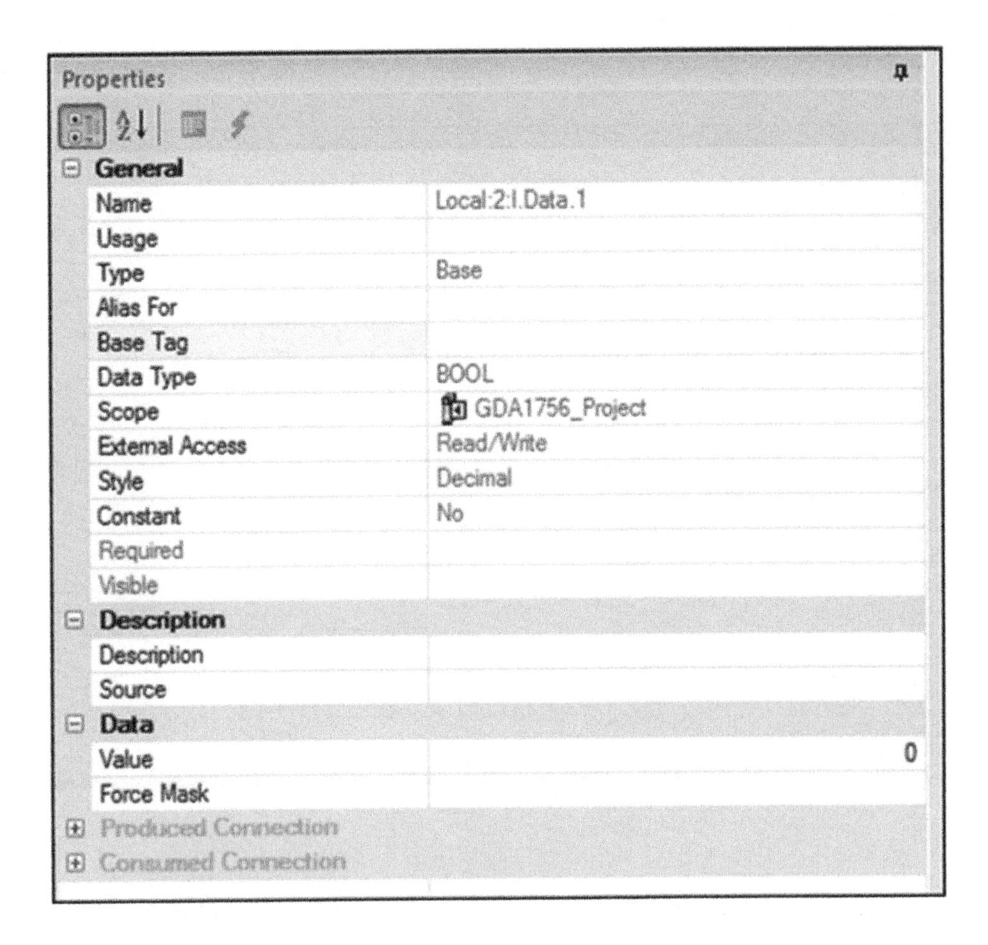

As you can see in this example of the *Data.1* terminal point, when a module is first installed, it automatically designates these input points as a **base tag,** with the scope set at the project level, which means it is controller scoped **(global)** rather than program scoped.

These terms will be discussed in the next section as we look into creating and editing tags, a topic not fully discussed as yet. This section on I/O addressing has mostly been about gaining a bit more understanding of the structural elements and addressing syntax.

Summary for Address Structure:

- When a module is added to the project, Studio 5000 automatically creates controller-scoped tags for the module.

- When a module is first added to the project, all its tags (addresses) are given base tag settings by default.

- The tag structure is dependent on the features of the particular module.

- Studio 5000 address structure is composed of five elements: Location, Slot, Type, Member, and Sub-Member or Bit.

- The four types of module data are: Input (I), Output (O), Configuration (C), and Status (S).

- Address tags are defined by the *Data Type* of the values they will store. Data Types include: BOOL, SINT, INT, DINT, and REAL.

- Data Types can also be a *Structured* or *pre-defined* Data Type: These include the Tag structure for Timer and Counter instructions, the PID instruction, and instructions that reference Arrays and Messages.

- Structured Data Types can contain several different data types within its overall structure.

- Structured Data Types can also be created or *User-Defined* to meet unique requirements of a project. All data related to one aspect of a system can be grouped together – regardless of having multiple data-types.

- Each tag is allocated a minimum of 32 bits regardless of the data type chosen, but will only use the number of bits determined by its data type setting.

UNDERSTANDING TAGS:

Tags are the method used by Studio 5000 software and the ControlLogix platform for providing simple text based names for referencing the address structures discussed in the previous section, and for the data stored in internal memory. After all, it's less tedious to key in a tag name, such as *Stop_PB*, instead of something like *Local: 2:I.Data.1.* Not only is it easier to do, it also allows you to be descriptive about the input connected to the module's terminal point. So we can give text-based names to input and output data points of the modules we've installed in our project, and also to the different control bits and instructions used in our logic. Like variables that are used in most other types of programming, a tag-name must be defined to let the controller know its attributes, and how to process and display the data it represents.

When looking into the subject of I/O addressing and tag creation, we often see the word "type" used in various ways to explain different aspects of the topic. For example, we started with the address structure that contained the *type attribute* – I, O, C, or S of the module itself, then moved into the topic of *data types* and then *structured data types*. In this section, I want to introduce the topic of *tag types*, along with other key terms that pertain to tags. Then we can look into examples of how to create tags; first for input or output modules like the ones in our example project, and then for some of the instructions we would normally use in ladder logic programming. But before going any further let's answer the basic question – what's the real benefit of using tags? After all – when we used symbols with our PLC instructions – didn't that serve the same purpose? The answer is *yes* and *no* – but mostly *no* – for a variety of reasons which I hope become clear by the end of this chapter.

Here are some of the reasons and benefits gained by using tags.

- In a Studio 5000 or RS Logix 5000 project, tags are the fundamental way of allocating, referencing and accessing memory.
- Tags are text-based variables, and so can be more descriptive in terms of function, location or device.
- Tags are stored within the controller memory after the project download, thus they automatically provide a basic level of documentation that resides in controller memory, rather than on the original programmer's computer as separate files.
- Tags can simplify and facilitate the programming process.
- Tags are alphabetically ordered and placed in the Tag Database of the project, making them easy to find and determine how they are used.
- The use of tags, makes it possible to show all the allocated memory that belongs to a given function, for instance the control of a pump motor, even though the tags may be defined with different data types.
- Tags can refer to a single stored element, a structure, or an array of values.

TAG TYPES:

Four types of tags can be created within the ControlLogix / Studio 5000 platform. It's important to understand these *types* because they define just how the tag will function or operate within your project.

- **Base Tag**: A base tag defines actual memory where data is stored. As mentioned earlier, base tags are *automatically* created for all *module* data structures. If not given a text-based name, then the initial base tag for a module will be a memory address, such as Local:3:I.Data.2. Descriptive names can also be assigned when using internal memory (bits) in logic instructions, and with *user-defined* or *structured data types* – like timers or counters. In these cases, the tag is a base tag rather than an alias.
- **Alias Tag**: An alias tag is a tag which represents another tag. The alias will mirror the data by pointing to the tag it represents.
- **Produced Tag**: A memory allocation with data that can be sent to another controller.
- **Consumed Tag**: A memory allocation that receives data from another controller.

TAG SYNTAX:

- Here are the basic syntax rules for creating tag-names:
- Useable characters are the letters: A –Z, a – z, 0 -9, and the underscore.
- Up to 40 characters can be used.
- Tags must begin with an alpha character or an underscore.
- Consecutive or trailing underscores are not allowed.
- Tags are not case sensitive – but for readability mixing upper & lower-case is recommended.

UNDERSTANDING SCOPE:

Whenever a tag is created, it must be defined as having either a *controller* or *program* scope. All tags created by the configuration of modules in your project are initially defined, by default, as controller scoped, but of course this can be changed to program scope by editing the tag. Scope refers to the areas of the project where a tag may be used, throughout the project in all programs - or only in one specific program. Program-scoped tags will reside in the Program Tags folder of the Program, while the Controller Tags folder will hold global tags that can be used by any of the programs within a project. *Controller scoped* tags are *global*; while *program scoped* tags are referred to as *local*. Here are some basic rules for determining how to assign the scope for a tag you create:

PROGRAM-SCOPE (LOCAL):

- Data at the program scope is isolated from other programs.
- Routines can't access data that is in the local-scope of another program.
- A local tag name may be used in multiple programs.

CONTROLLER-SCOPE (GLOBAL):

- You want to use the tag (and data) in multiple programs within the project
- In a MSG instruction
- To communicate with a PanelView Terminal
- To use as a producer or consumer tag
- If used as an Axis data-type

CREATING BASE & ALIAS TAGS:

If you double-click on the *Controller Tags* folder, the *Monitor Tags* tab should show something that resembles the screenshot below. As you can see, the basic address structure is in place for each of the modules created in our sample project.

These address structures, visible for each property, and when expanded for each terminal point, is essentially a group of base tags. Also notice that each of these tags are currently set to a *global* or *controller-scope* – the GDA1756_Project.

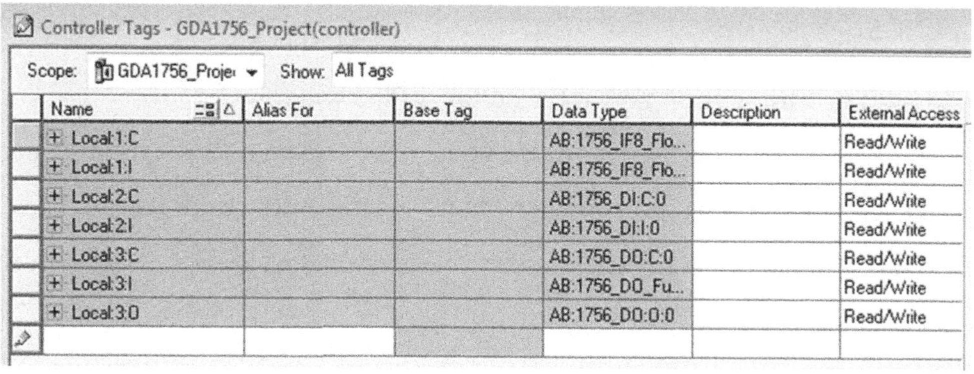

Controller Tags - GDA1756_Project(controller)

Scope: GDA1756_Proje Show: All Tags

Name	Alias For	Base Tag	Data Type	Description	External Access
+ Local:1:C			AB:1756_IF8_Flo...		Read/Write
+ Local:1:I			AB:1756_IF8_Flo...		Read/Write
+ Local:2:C			AB:1756_DI:C:0		Read/Write
+ Local:2:I			AB:1756_DI:I:0		Read/Write
+ Local:3:C			AB:1756_DO:C:0		Read/Write
+ Local:3:I			AB:1756_DO_Fu...		Read/Write
+ Local:3:O			AB:1756_DO:O:0		Read/Write

At this point, there are no descriptions or alias tag names – the address structure alone is considered the base tag. The relationship between names, base tags and alias tags will become more obvious as we begin creating tag-names in the examples that follow.

If we want to program any type of useful control function, we'll need to add some details in order to make the I/O modules - and other programming instructions, something we can reference and use. Consider the following *untagged* program logic that might be used for control in a simple *Emergency Stop* routine.

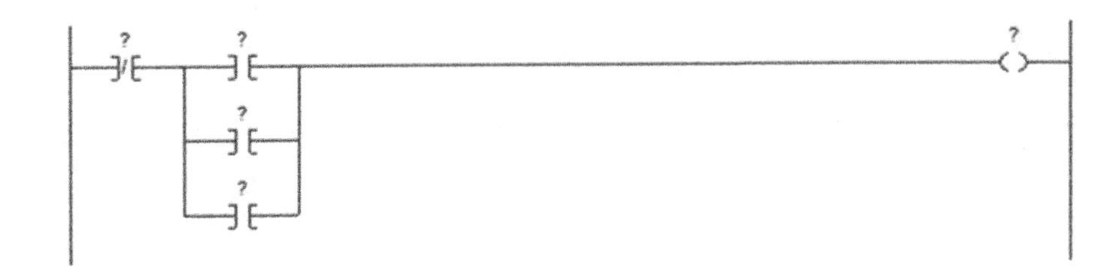

In the example that follows, we have I/O modules which are configured for use, but we still need to assign our logic instructions with appropriate addressing that will reference specific terminals or internal memory. Here is one of the common methods of accomplishing this objective.

METHOD 1 ADDRESSING:

- Go to the **Tag Editor** (Edit tab) at the bottom of the window.
- Remember to establish the *scope* for the tag you are creating. If program scope is selected, choose from the drop-down menu to select the desired program. The created tag will reside in the program tags folder of that program. Controller scope for this example is GDA1756_Project.
- Enter a tag name into the field at the bottom of the list. Remember – the tags you create will group alphabetically.

Enter a Tag Name to use as an Alias for a Base Tag

Controller Tags - GDA1756_Project(controller)

Scope: GDA1756_Proje Show: All Tags

Name	Alias For	Base Tag	Data Type	Description	External Access
+ Local:1:C			AB:1756_IF8_Flo...		Read/Write
+ Local:1:I			AB:1756_IF8_Flo...		Read/Write
+ Local:2:C			AB:1756_DI:C:0		Read/Write
+ Local:2:I			AB:1756_DI:I:0		Read/Write
+ Local:3:C			AB:1756_DO:C:0		Read/Write
+ Local:3:I			AB:1756_DO_Fu...		Read/Write
+ Local:3:O			AB:1756_DO:O:0		Read/Write

Tab to the *Alias For* column and select from the drop-down menu a property, or data point. Notice that the Base Tag column now holds the address structure since the text-based name, **Estop_1**, has been entered into the name column.

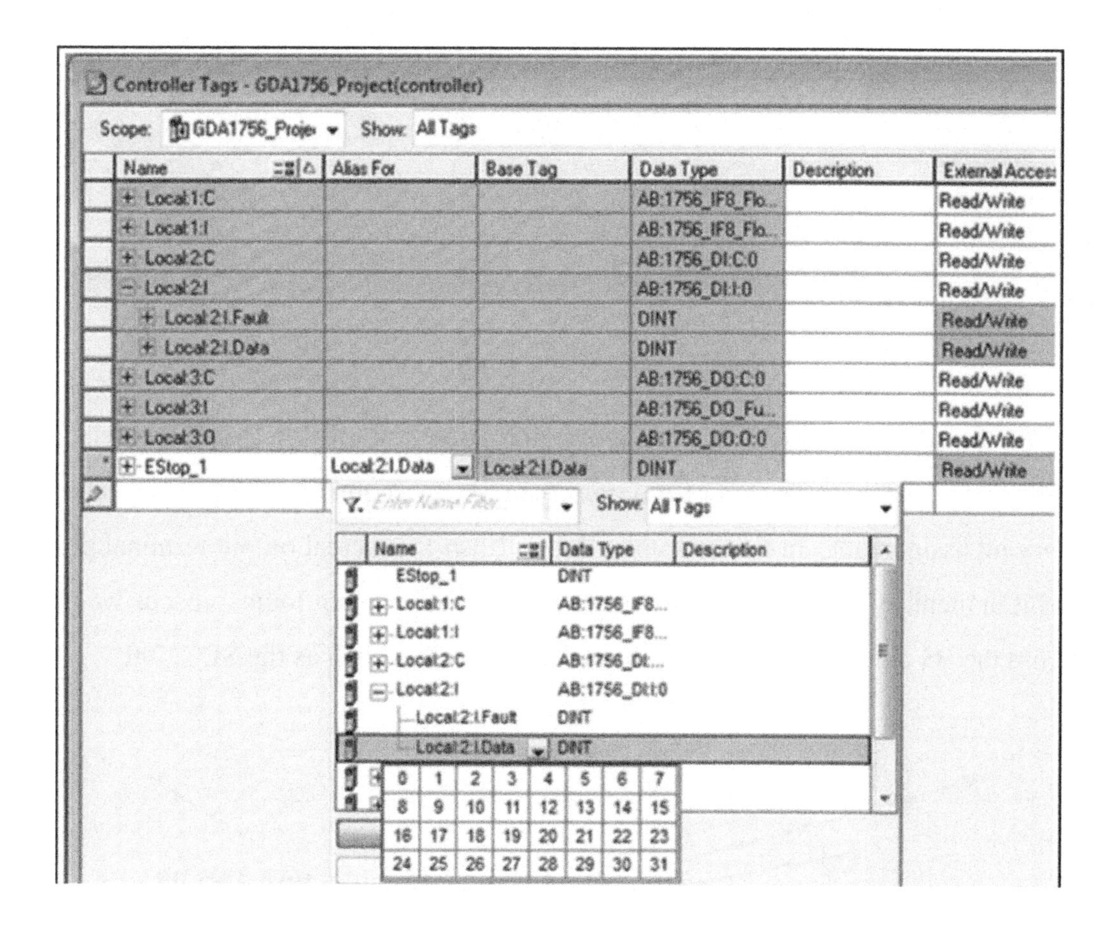

Enter a description (optional), and select binary from the *Style* column since this is a BOOL data type and we're looking to see a change-of-state on a digital input terminal.

In the <u>Alias For</u> field, choose the terminal / bit from the drop-down menu. Enter a <u>description</u> (optional) and select the <u>style</u> (binary).

Controller Tags - GDA1756_Project(controller)

Scope: GDA1756_Proje Show: All Tags

Name	Alias For	Base Tag	Data Type	Description	External Access	Constant	Style
+ Local:1:C			AB:1756_IF8_Flo...		Read/Write		
+ Local:1:I			AB:1756_IF8_Flo...		Read/Write		
+ Local:2:C			AB:1756_DI:C:0		Read/Write		
+ Local:2:I			AB:1756_DI:I:0		Read/Write		
+ Local:3:C			AB:1756_DO:C:0		Read/Write		
+ Local:3:I			AB:1756_DO_Fu...		Read/Write		
+ Local:3:O			AB:1756_DO:O:0		Read/Write		
EStop_1	Local:2:I.Data.0	Local:2:I.Data.0	BOOL	Emergency Stop ...	Read/Write		Binary
EStop_2	Local:2:I.Data.1	Local:2:I.Data.1	BOOL	Emergency Stop	Read/Write		Binary
EStop_Reset	Local:2:I.Data.3	Local:2:I.Data.3	BOOL	EStop_Reset	Read/Write		Binary

After you have created ladder logic in a program routine – simply click on the instruction question mark **[?]** to assign a tag from those you have just created, or to use an internal memory bit assignment. In this example, the OTE isn't an actual output terminal point, just a bit in memory we want to use in other parts of the program logic – just as we used bits from the B3 datafile when programming legacy PLC's such as the SLC-500.

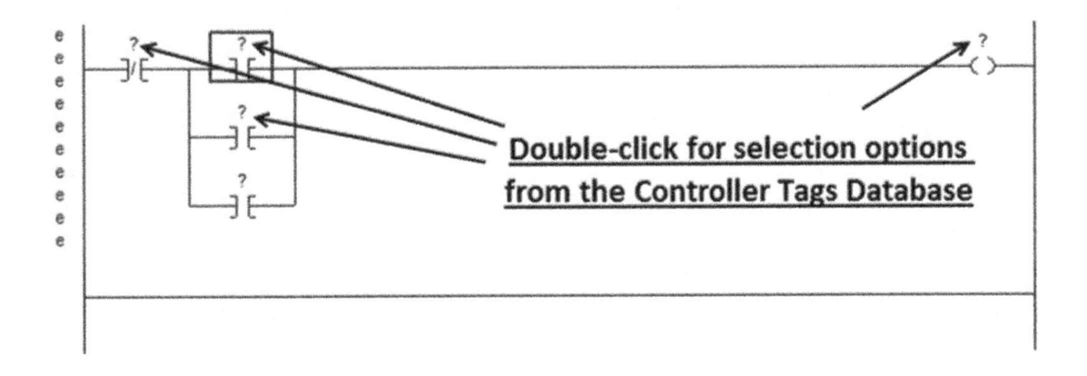

By clicking on each of the question marks in our ladder rung, we can select tags we have previously created in the Tag Editor. When finished, our logic should look more like the following example which shows both base and alias tag names.

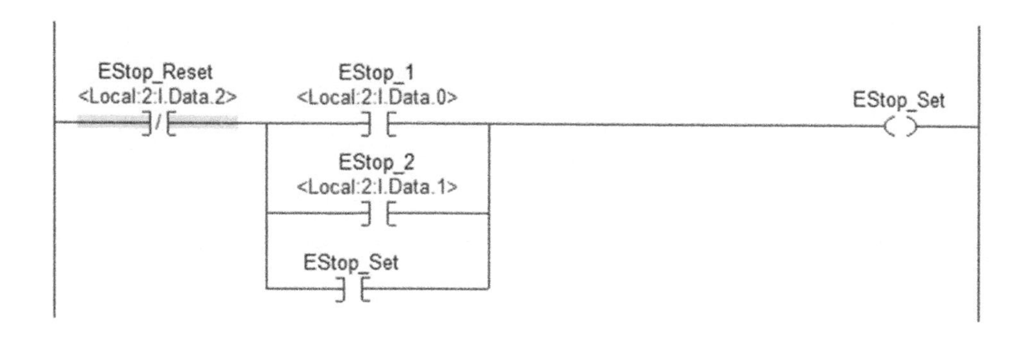

Note that the output, **Estop_Set**, is an internal memory bit. It is <u>not an alias for anything else</u> and so is essentially a <u>base tag name</u>. It doesn't require an entry in the *Alias For* field; we simply name the bit of memory and select the BOOL data type, to create this tag using the Tag Editor.

Next is an example, using this same method of addressing, to create a tag name for a timer, which is a structured data type. The timer tag name is essentially a base-tag, as there isn't any real need to assign an alias to a timer or counter. Their control words and bits can be referenced in program logic by the base tag name – although an alias can be defined to reference the timer (or control-bits), it usually isn't considered to be a good programming practice.

Here I've created a base-tag name, "*Media_Use_Time*", for a control application where I need to monitor the length of time that a blast media is used, and flag the operator when it requires changing. Just like creating the other tags, we click into the bottom Name field (lower left) and enter whatever name we want for the timer – remember, normal rules of syntax still apply for all tag names.

+ Local:3:O			AB:1756_DO:O:0
+ EStop_1	Local:2:I.Data	Local:2:I.Data	DINT
Media_Use_Time			TIMER

After creating the name, click over to the Data Type column, and from the drop-down menu select TIMER as the data type. As you can see, there are many other data types, regular and structured, from which to choose.

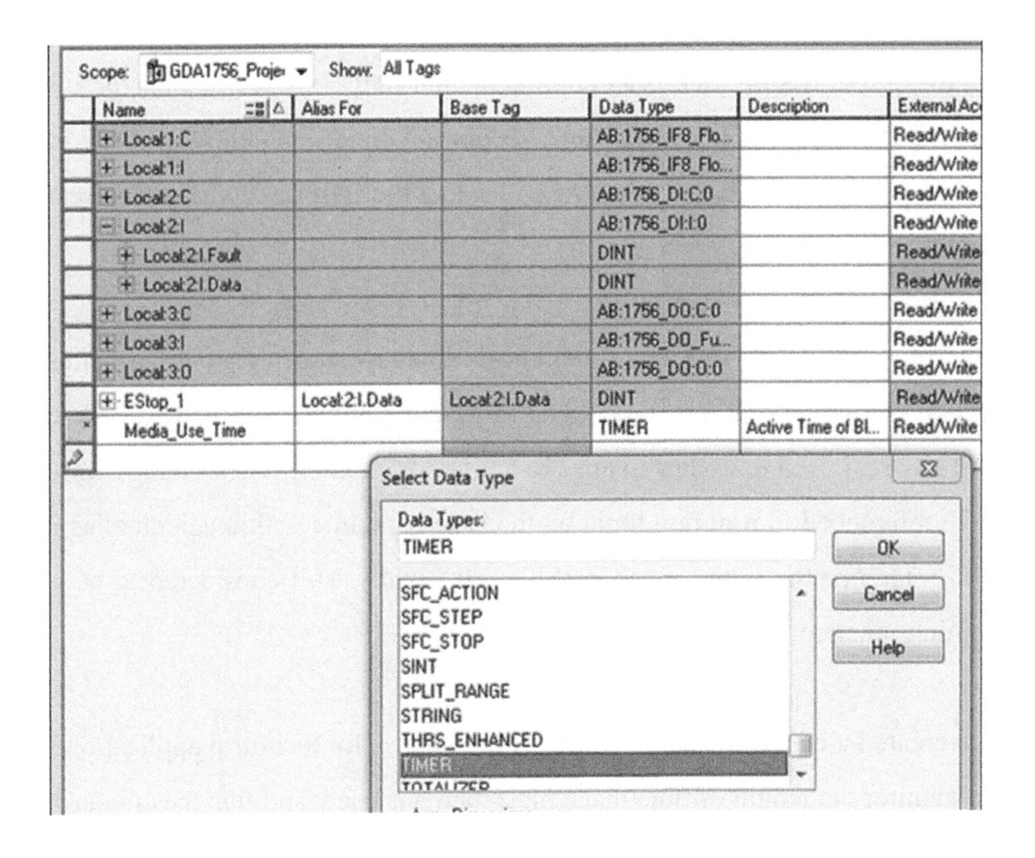
Scope: GDA1756_Proje Show: All Tags

Name	Alias For	Base Tag	Data Type	Description	External Ac
+ Local:1:C			AB:1756_IF8_Flo...		Read/Write
+ Local:1:I			AB:1756_IF8_Flo...		Read/Write
+ Local:2:C			AB:1756_DI:C:0		Read/Write
- Local:2:I			AB:1756_DI:I:0		Read/Write
+ Local:2:I.Fault			DINT		Read/Write
+ Local:2:I.Data			DINT		Read/Write
+ Local:3:C			AB:1756_DO:C:0		Read/Write
+ Local:3:I			AB:1756_DO_Fu...		Read/Write
+ Local:3:O			AB:1756_DO:O:0		Read/Write
+ EStop_1	Local:2:I.Data	Local:2:I.Data	DINT		Read/Write
Media_Use_Time			TIMER	Active Time of Bl...	Read/Write

After clicking [OK], if you go to the *Monitor Tags* tab and expand the ***Media_Use_Time*** timer - you should see the following timer structure showing all its elements and its individual data types.

- Media_Use_Time	{...}	{...}		TIMER
+ Media_Use_Time.PRE	0		Decimal	DINT
+ Media_Use_Time.ACC	0		Decimal	DINT
Media_Use_Time.EN	0		Decimal	BOOL
Media_Use_Time.TT	0		Decimal	BOOL
Media_Use_Time.DN	0		Decimal	BOOL

Once again, as you enter program logic, you can assign your created tags to the instructions in your program, as shown here.

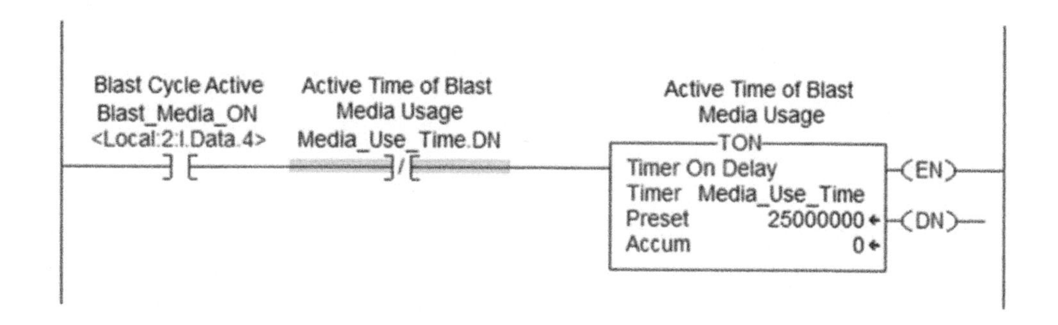

Whenever the *Monitor Tags* or *Tag Editor* screen is selected, the Properties box is displayed on the right-side of the computer screen. It details the settings made for the address structure you have selected on the monitor or edit screen. Just for comparison – here is a before and after screenshot of one of the data points, for which we have created an alias tag.

Properties Box before and after assigning tag names for <Local:2:I.Data.2>

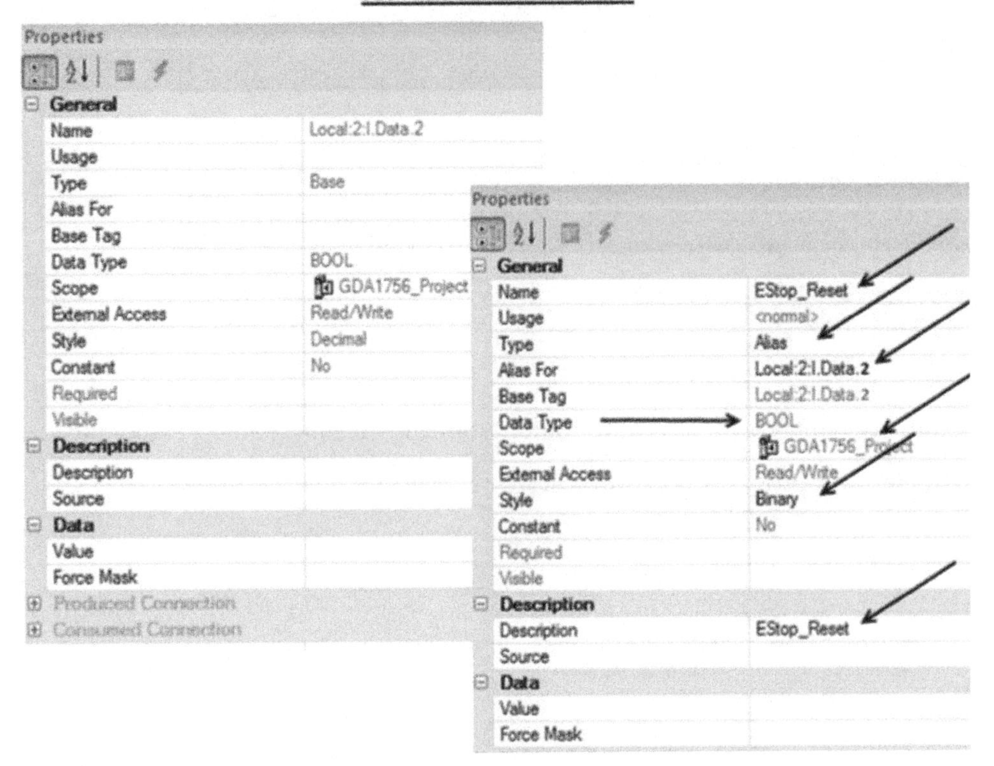

As you can see, there are numerous differences between the default base tag, initially created by the software, and the newly created alias tag. As stated earlier, tag types determine how a tag will operate within your project. This includes which programs or controllers have access to the tag, the type of data it will contain and how that data can be used or displayed.

Another relatively easy method of creating and assigning tags, is to do it as you program instruction elements within your project. In the example below, I show this basic method of creating tag names for several types of logic instructions. Whenever an instruction is selected and placed within a rung, you will see the highlighted question mark [**?**] appear inside the instruction frame. By doing a right-click on the question-mark, an option selection box appears having the option for *New Tag* at the top. Choosing *New Tag* from this menu, allows you to name a base tag, assign it as an alias, and define the scope of the tag and its data type – essentially all the things you would do using the Tag Editor, as in the previous examples. Here are several rungs of program logic and screenshots illustrating this method of tag creation.

METHOD 2 ADDRESSING:

- Right-click the [?] in the instruction field, select *New Tag* and the following options menu appears, allowing you to define a new tag for this instruction. This could be a simple start-up routine so I'll call this tag "System_Start".

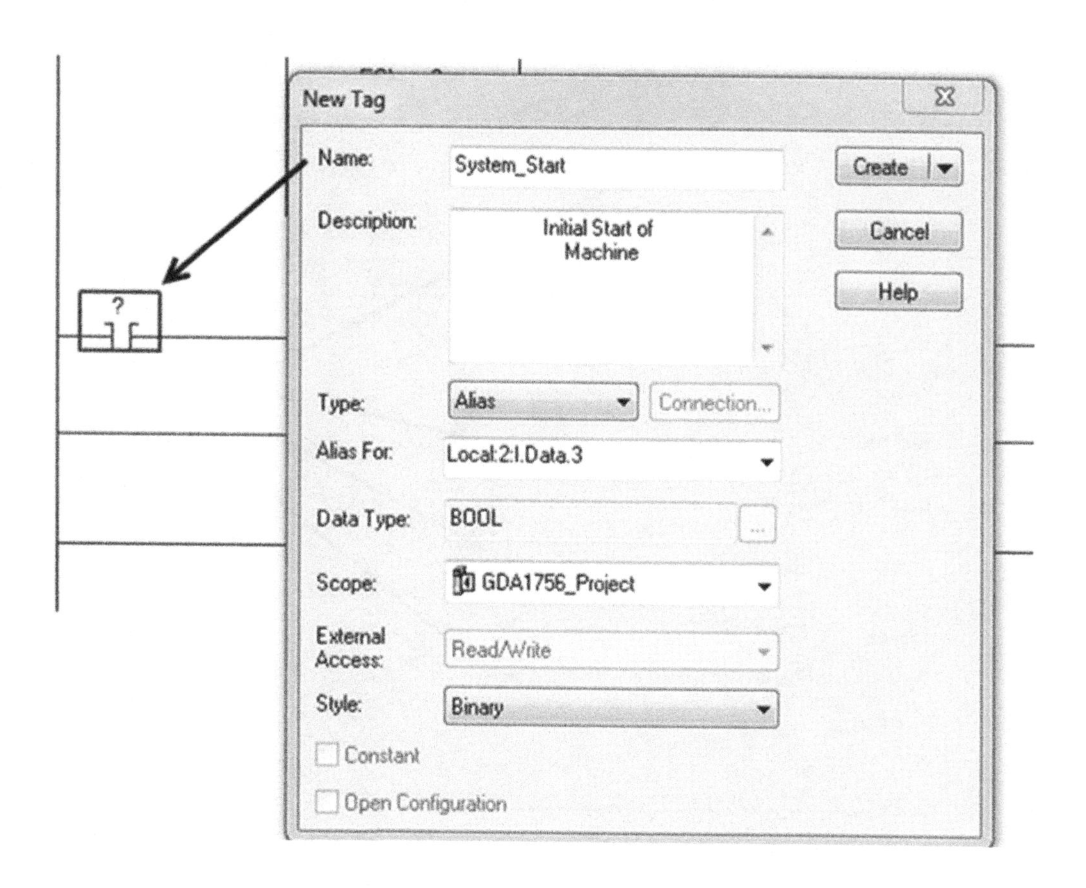

- The XIC or "*examine if closed*" instruction shown, will change states based on a physical input wired into the input module in slot 2 of our project. I'll give this instruction an alias name of "System_Start" and link it to the base tag of Local: 2:I.Data.3. I've defined it with a controller (global) scope and BOOL data type.

- In the next illustration, I want to create a tag for the OTE instruction on the same rung. I've elected, just for the sake of showing a different example, not to make this OTE a physical output but instead an internal memory bit. Tag creation is much the same as shown for the XIC example – the one major difference being that we leave the data type as a base tag and do not make it an <u>*Alias For*</u> any other tag. I've named this tag *Machine_Ready*.

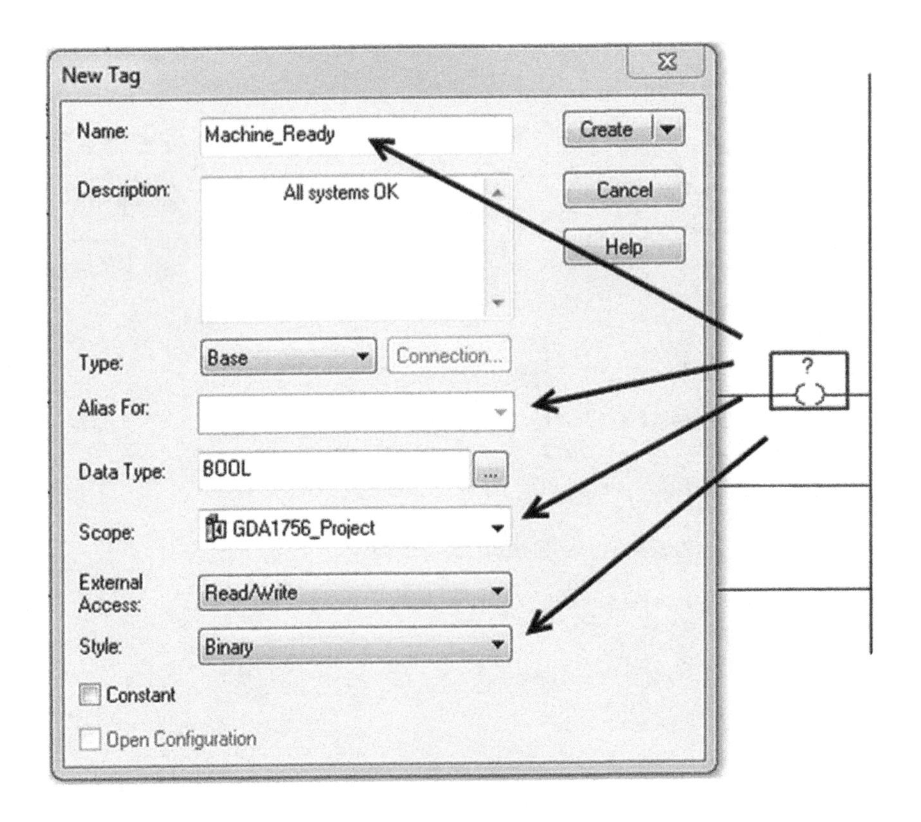

- The newly created tag, *Machine_Ready*, is further defined as a BOOL data type, having a Controller-scope, and a binary value. When selections are finished, click on the [Create] button.

In the following rungs, you can see these items as they now appear. In addition to the XIC and OTE instructions just shown, I've added a timer, used one of the timer control bits, and some additional data points from our input module – all with tags created using this second method.

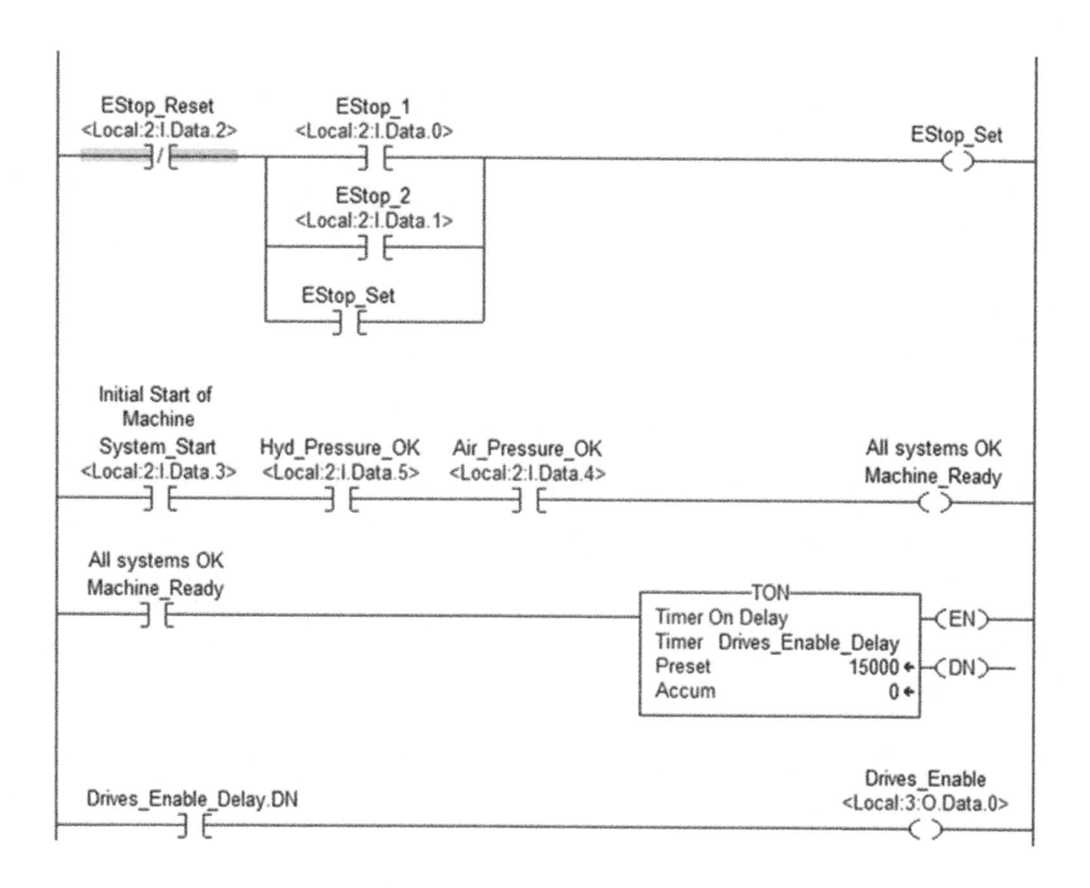

As you can see from this example, descriptions can be included on tags, and are now displayed in the ladder logic, along with the alias and base tag names.

Obviously, one method isn't necessarily preferable over the other; this is only to show that, as you build a project, there is some flexibility when creating tags, assigning aliases, and editing descriptions or other properties. Here is a brief summary for some of the relevant details of tag creation and usage.

Summary for Addressing & Tag Creation:

- All tags have a base tag name, but can also have an alias that references them. The alias tag points the program to the base tag that contains the actual data.

- Base tags have allocated memory for data storage, alias tags do not.

- All tags must be defined by scope and data type.

- When I/O modules are configured for the project, the Logix5000 software automatically creates base tag names using the address structure and gives them a controller (global) scope.

- Multiple aliases can refer to the same base tag. This is not considered to be a good programming practice. If multiple aliases have been used in a project you can use the *Cross Reference Tool & Tag Hierarchy* selection to get a view of the alias names that are linked.

- Tags can be created or edited from the *Tag Editor,* and values monitored from the *Tag Monitor* displays.

- An alias tag can also refer to another alias tag. Once again, not considered a good programming technique.

HANDS-ON EXERCISE

In one of the routines within your example project:

1. Create a ladder routine similar to the one shown on page 81, or one of your own choosing.

2. Address instructions within your ladder logic using the methods shown in the previous sections; Method 1 and Method 2. Refer to page 72 – 80.

3. Practice the assignment of "alias" tags and creating base tag names for BOOL memory allocations.

Creating Produced & Consumed Tags:

The next tag types we need to consider are called *Produced* and *Consumed* tags. These important tag types provide a method for sharing data between different controllers on a single network. This transfer of data is set to occur according to configured RPI intervals of the receiving controllers, and doesn't require the use of program logic to send or receive. Here is a simple diagram of several controllers in a network, such as an EtherNet/IP network, that could share data by the use of produced and consumed tags.

Typical network topology for shared system data tags.

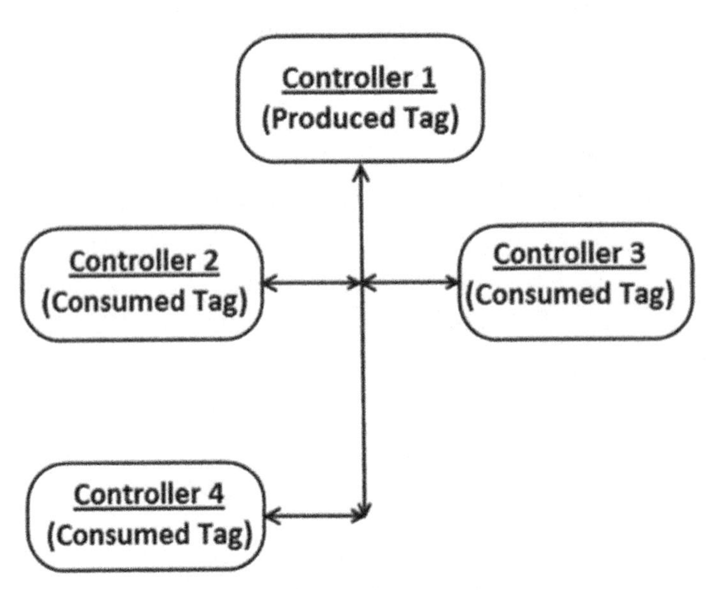

Produced Tags **are broadcast**
Consumed Tags **are received**
A Produced Tag and its corresponding Consumed Tag must be configured as the same data type.

A producer tag contains the data to be sent or broadcast – from Controller 1 in this illustration. The consumer tag is configured in Controllers 2, 3 and 4 – and will receive the data. In other words, any data produced by one controller needs a "place to call home" at its consumer location. The consumed tag provides that place, on each receiving controller, by defining a name and data type so the data can be stored and used by the logic on that particular controller (the consumer).

All the controllers on a network can have both produced and consumed tags, which is why I've shown arrows on the above diagram pointing in both directions. In the illustration, Controller 1 holds a produced tag that will be broadcast to Controllers 2, 3 and 4. Controller 1 might also hold a consumed tag for a produced tag that will originate and be broadcast from Controller 4. Controller 2 and 3 might have the corresponding consumer tags for a Controller 4 produced tag. While this might seem a bit confusing, it should become more understandable after seeing how these tags are created – which is the main objective of this section. Still, it is helpful to understand how and why these tags are used in real-world applications.

Creating a produced tag is fairly straightforward, while creating the complementary consumed tag usually takes a few more steps. Remember, we'll need to set-up communication modules in both the producer and consumer controllers, configure them with proper IP addressing and some other details – before our two controllers will be able to communicate and pass information.

For a simple example, let's say we want to use the following ladder logic to pass along the accumulated value of a counter to another controller that is actually controlling a conveyor system, and located in a remote area of a manufacturing plant. The tag,

Part_Count_Limit, can be the produced tag, available to the other controller, the consumer, on its network. Here is an example showing the I/O Configuration for the *Producer* Controller and the basic steps needed to create this producer tag.

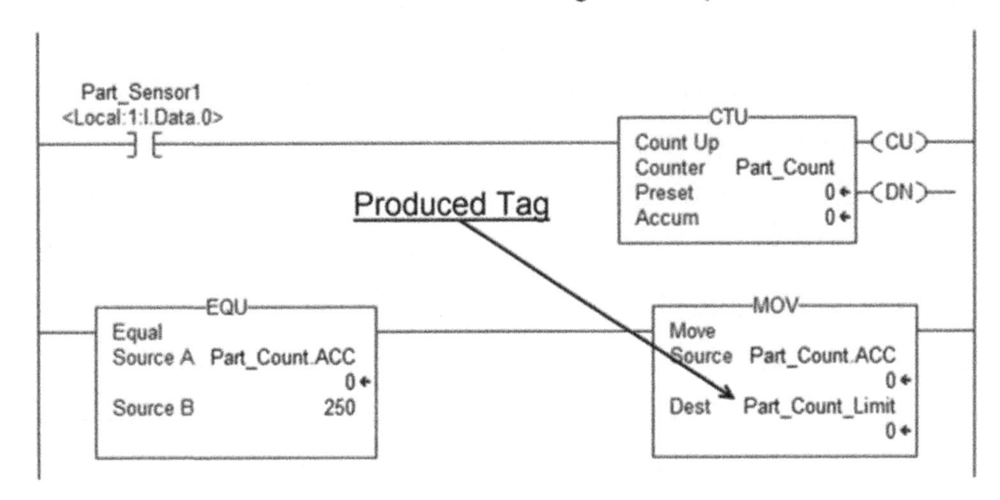

CREATING A PRODUCED TAG:

In the I/O Configuration of the *producer controller*, I've configured a 1756-ENBT module to connect our controller to a network. We need to note several details at this point, specifically the slot position of the communication module and other information pertaining to the controller module, a 1756-L71 with 10 slots. This information will be necessary later when setting up the consumer controller and creating a consumed tag.

This is the basic I/O configuration for the project controller which I've named: *GDA_Producer_Controller*. As you can see, it contains several modules including the 1756-ENBT communication module in slot 4 - which I've set with an IP address of 192.168.25.110 – also a detail we'll need when setting up the other controller in our network.

Producer Controller I/O Configuration

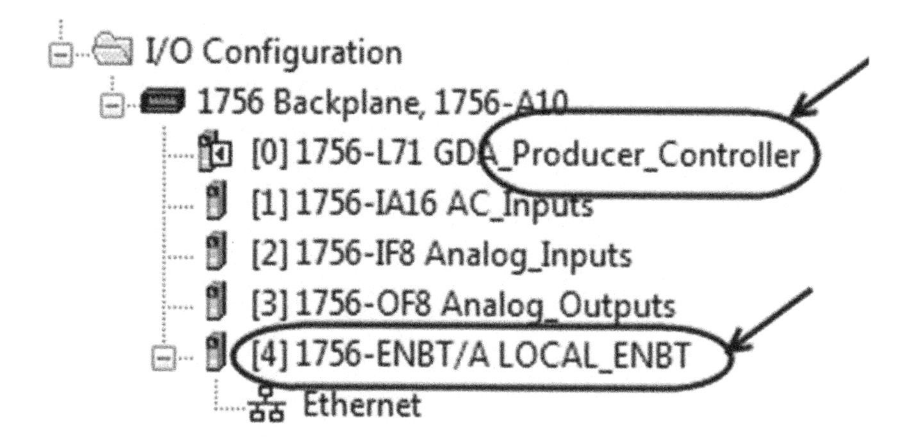

- To create the Produced Tag: Right-click on the *Controller Tags* folder and select the *Tag Editor*.

- Right-click on the tag you want to make a producer; or as shown in this example, create an entirely new tag by typing in the name in the bottom name field of the Tag Editor. I've chosen the name "Part_Count_Limit" for the new tag and selected a data type of DINT.

Scope: GDA_Producer_C Show: All Tags

Name	Alias For	Base Tag	Data Type
Conveyor_Stop			BOOL
+ Producer_ENBT:I			AB:1756_ENET_
+ Producer_ENBT:O			AB:1756_ENET_
Part_Count_Limit			DINT

- Right-click the new tag-name to bring up the *Tag Properties* menu – you can then define the tag as a **produced** tag, and set-up the connection details as shown in the following examples. An alternate method of creating a new tag can be accomplished while programming ladder logic. This was shown in the previous section as **Method 2**, and involves doing a right-click on the question mark [**?**] next to the Destination parameter of the MOV instruction, and selecting ***New Tag.*** This would bring up the *Tag Properties* menu as well, allowing you to name and define the new produced tag.

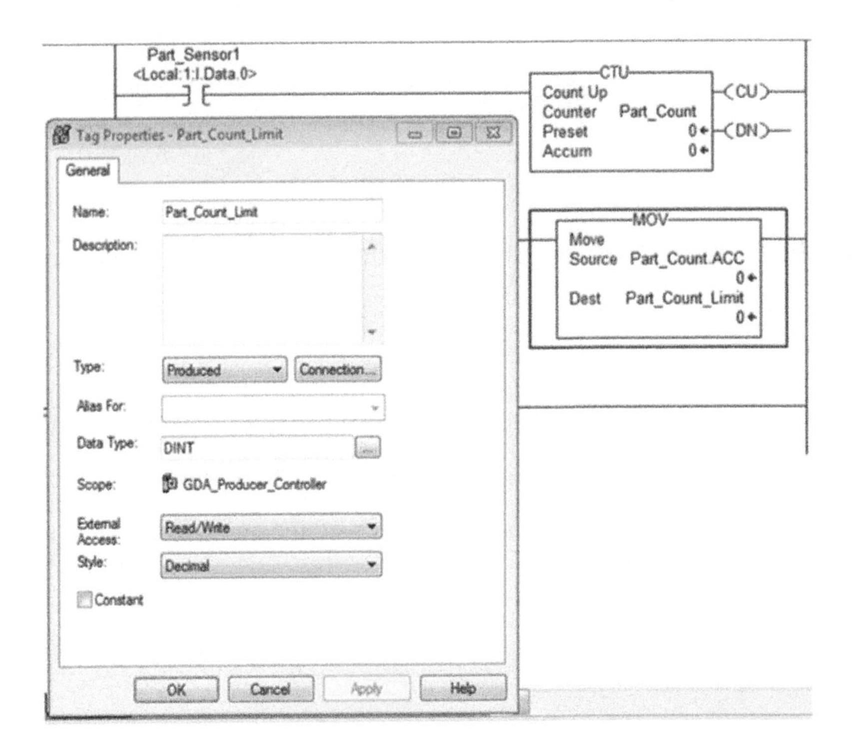

- After selecting the **Produced** tag type and setting the data type for DINT, click on the *Connection* button. This will allow you to set the number of consumers that will be receiving this data. For this example, it is set for only one other controller. The Connection button option becomes available whenever a produced or consumed tag type is selected as the tag type on the Tag Properties menu. Also note the *Advanced* selection button, which offers options for setting an RPI interval range.

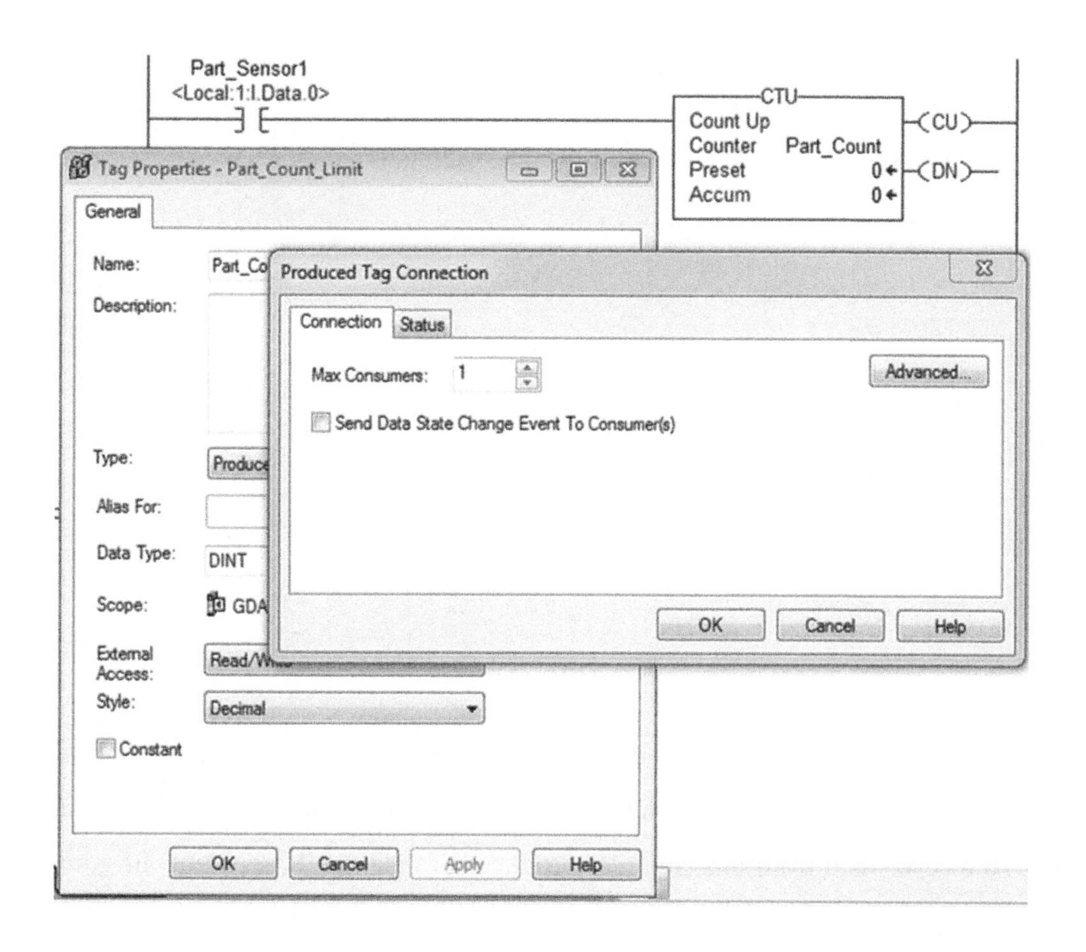

- Click OK to finish the set-up for the producer tag.

CONFIGURATION FOR THE CONSUMED TAG:

Creating the corresponding consumed tag – for the most part, follows the same basic steps used to create the produced tag. However, some additional I/O configuration must also be done in the consumer controller. What follows, are the necessary steps for setting up the Consumer controller, named *GDA_Consumer_Controller*, and then creating the consumer tag, *Part_Count_Limit*.

First of all, here is a basic ladder logic example, yet untagged, that could be programmed into the *consumer controller* to utilize our producer tag data.

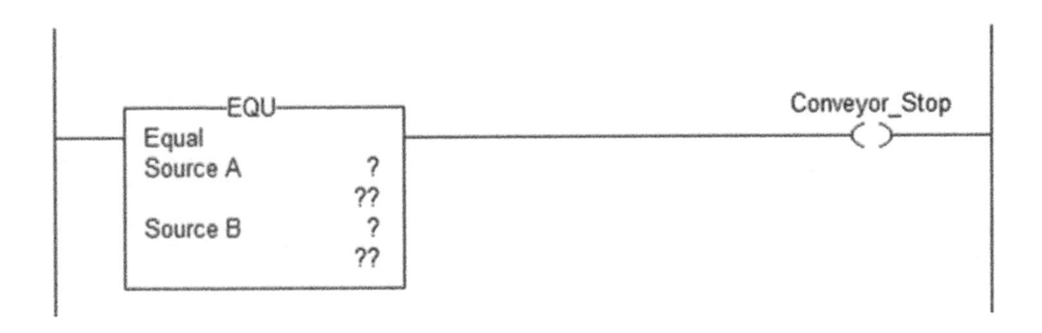

This type of rung logic could be used to stop a conveyor system, based on data that is derived and broadcast from another controller, remotely located within our manufacturing plant. To receive data from this (*remote)* producer of data, we'll need to configure our consumer (*local)* controller. Here are the basic steps involved in adding the producer controller to the consumer controller's I/O configuration.

CONFIGURE THE CONSUMER CONTROLLER:

- Add a communication module to the consumer controller. Go to the *I/O Configuration* folder, right-click to bring up the option for *New Module* to select a communication module. I've selected a 1756-ENBT – just like on the producer controller. I've configured the module to have an IP address of 192.168.25.111.

- Add the communication module that is configured in the producer controller (remote), to the I/O configuration of the consumer controller. It should be added as a "child" of the consumer's communication module – so highlight the 1756-ENBT module, right-click and then choose the *New Module* option.

- Add the producer controller, "GDA_Producer_Controller" to the I/O configuration of the consumer controller. It should be added as a "child" of the producer's network communication module – the 1756-ENBT in slot 4. Remember, it was a 1756-L71 located in slot 0.

Consumer Controller I/O Configuration

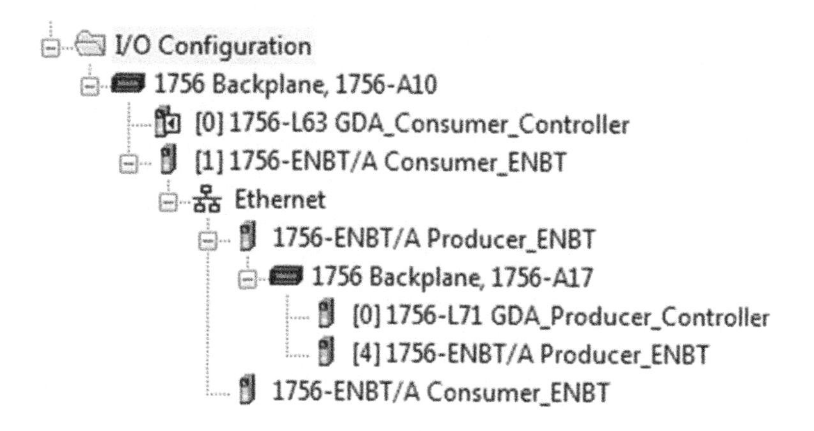

The communication pathway, step-by-step, starting from the perspective of the consumer controller, can be seen from this configuration model: the produced tag (data) from the producer controller > producer controller's backplane > producer controllers ENBT module > Ethernet Media > Consumer controller's ENBT > Consumer controller (memory & logic programs).

CREATE THE CONSUMER TAG:

- To create the actual tag: Right-click *Controller Tags* folder and the *Tag Editor.* Enter the name for the consumed tag – just as in our other examples, in the bottom line name field.

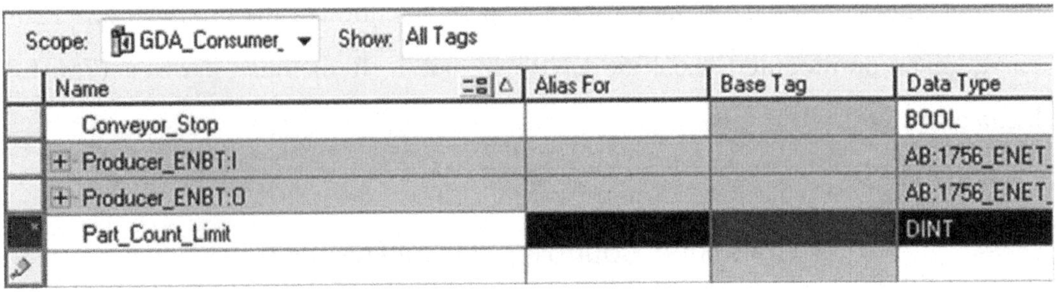

Scope: GDA_Consumer_ Show: All Tags

Name	Alias For	Base Tag	Data Type
Conveyor_Stop			BOOL
+ Producer_ENBT:I			AB:1756_ENET_
+ Producer_ENBT:O			AB:1756_ENET_
Part_Count_Limit			DINT

- Right-click on the new tag-name, and choose the *Edit "Part_Count_Limit" Properties* option from the menu selections.

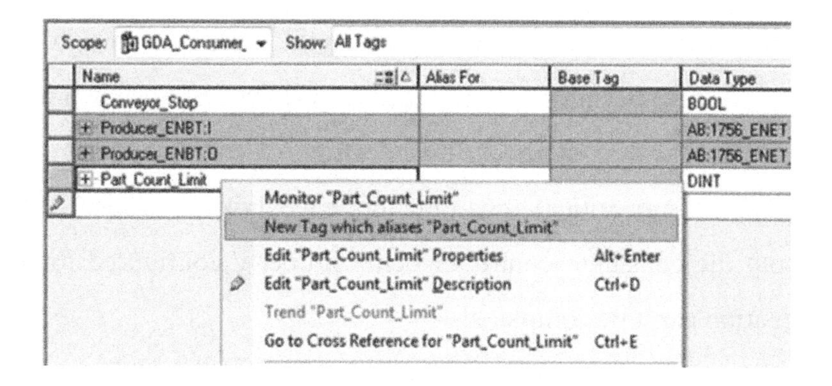

When the Tag Properties box is displayed, the tag-name and data type should already be filled. Use the following as general steps in filling out each part of the tag properties. Make the tag a *Consumed* tag type, click on the *Connection* button and give the *name of the producer controller*, the *producer tag-name*, and *set the RPI interval* for the consumer controller to receive the data. The only other selection I've made to the properties of this Consumed tag is to make it *Read Only* regarding External Access. This protects the data to a greater degree once it is received.

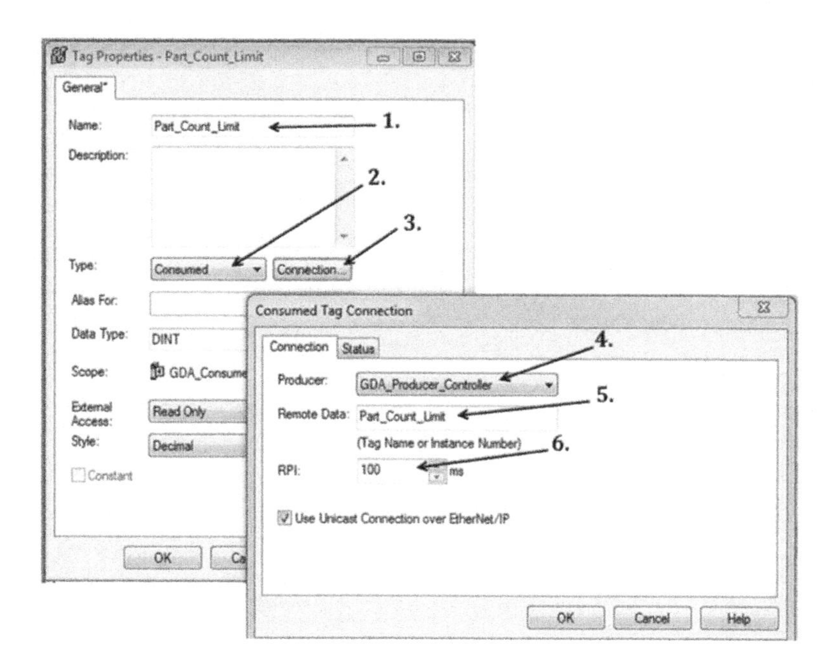

Note that if the producer controller isn't set-up correctly in the consumer controller's I/O Configuration, it will not appear in the Producer drop-down menu shown in step 4. I'm just reiterating that the first steps in this section, where we performed the I/O configuration changes, are critical regarding how we link controllers together on a network. Without the consumer controller being properly configured for its network, consumer tag creation can't be completed.

Here again, is the earlier view of the consumer controller logic – just a simple example of how the sharing of data between two or more controllers might be utilized in different types of manufacturing operations.

In this scenario, whenever "*Part_Count_Limit*" reaches the source B value of 250, it causes the *Conveyor_Stop* bit to become "true". This bit can then be used to stop the conveyor system, as its name implies, until some other condition occurs - or in any number of other operations within the logic of the program.

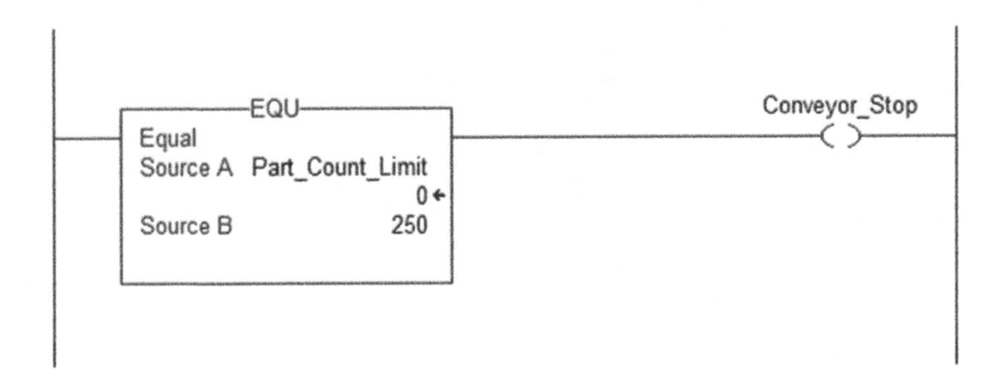

Summary for Produced & Consumed Tags

- Produced and Consumed tags are a method used in the ControlLogix platform to share data between different controllers over a network.

- Produced and consumed tags are created at a controller (global) scope.

- Produced and consumed tags can be created from the Controller Tags folder > Tag Editor >Edit Properties, and also directly from the ladder logic if creating a new tag.

- A produced tag is broadcast and received as a consumed tag, on a timed interval (RPI) configured on the consumer controller.

- Don't set RPI times faster than the network update time (NUT) of the network. Try to set RPI time to the highest permissible timing that works for your application.

- A produced tag is broadcast - without the use of program logic instructions.

- A consumer controller must have a targeted device (controller) in its I/O Configuration for it to consume tag data from another controller.

- If there is more than one consumer receiving a produced tag, then all consumers should normally be set with the same RPI value to prevent intermittent loss of data.

- Controllers can be both producers *and* consumers of data from other network controllers, but can't be a consumer of their own produced tag.

- A controller can't be both a producer and consumer of its produced tag.

- Data types that are allowed for produced and consumed tags are the double-integer (DINT) and floating-point (REAL). These data types can also be set-up as an array, such as DINT[30]. Also user-defined structured data types can be used to send multiple tags to a single controller.

- The producer tag and its corresponding consumer tag must be the same data type.

- Limit the size of a producer/consumer tag to 500 bytes.

- Every produced tag uses connections in the controller equal to: 1 plus (+) the number of its consumers. Every consumer tag uses 1 connection in its controller.

1. Add a -ENBT communication module to your I/O configuration.

2. Perform basic configuration and assign an IP address for a network. For example the 192.168.25.110 network address used in my example. This was for the "Producer" controller I/O configuration.

3. Create a Produced Tag following steps shown on pages 86 - 89. Note that while my example was for a DINT data type, the produced tag could be for a single BOOL element as well.

4. While on the Tag Properties menu, remember to use the Connections Tab where the number of "Consumers" will be defined.

5. Create a Consumer project I/O configuration as shown on page 91. In this example I've used a L6 controller and a 1756-ENBT module.

6. Set the IP address for the Consumer ENBT for the same network as the Producer controller ENBT, example: 192.168.25.111.

7. Add the Producer Controller to the I/O configuration of the Consumer Controller, page 91. Note that it should be added as a "child" of the Consumer Controller's ENBT module.

8. Create the Consumer Tag on the Consumer Controller, pages 92 - 93.

CREATING & USING ADD-ON INSTRUCTIONS:

These custom instructions, "AOI's", are versatile and fairly straightforward to use. They are essentially user-defined logic routines created to solve unique, program specific types of problems. When placed into a routine, they execute similar to a subroutine, but without the requirement of using a (JSR) to call a subroutine. It becomes a custom instruction which you can then select from the instruction bar and place in different routines throughout the project, use multiple times in the same routine, or export to other projects as well.

Here is an example of an Add-On Instruction I've named RUNTIME, used to total the curing time for a process. It could be modified for any number of uses that require monitoring the runtime hours on equipment or processes.

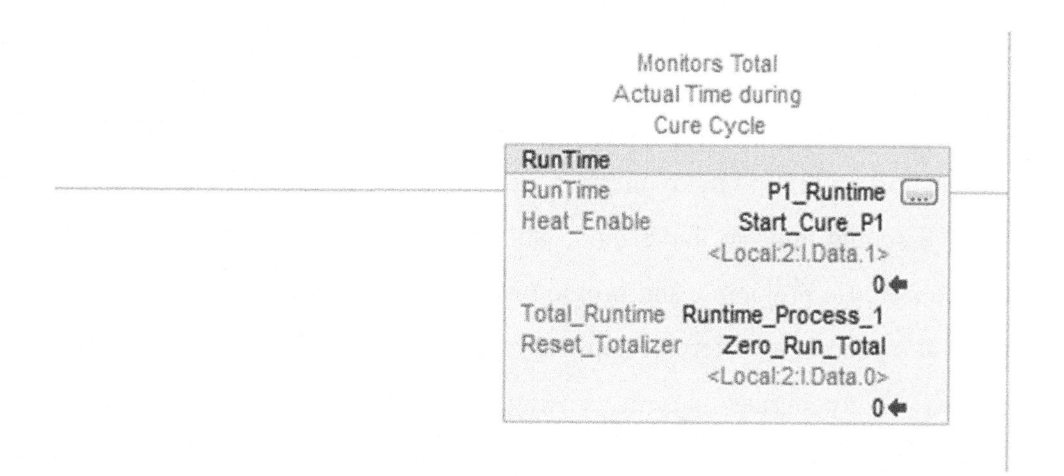

Next shown, is the actual ladder logic that creates the Runtime AOI instruction shown in this example. As you can see, it's made up of only five rungs of logic in a timer/counter arrangement that computes a floating point value called *Total_Runtime*.

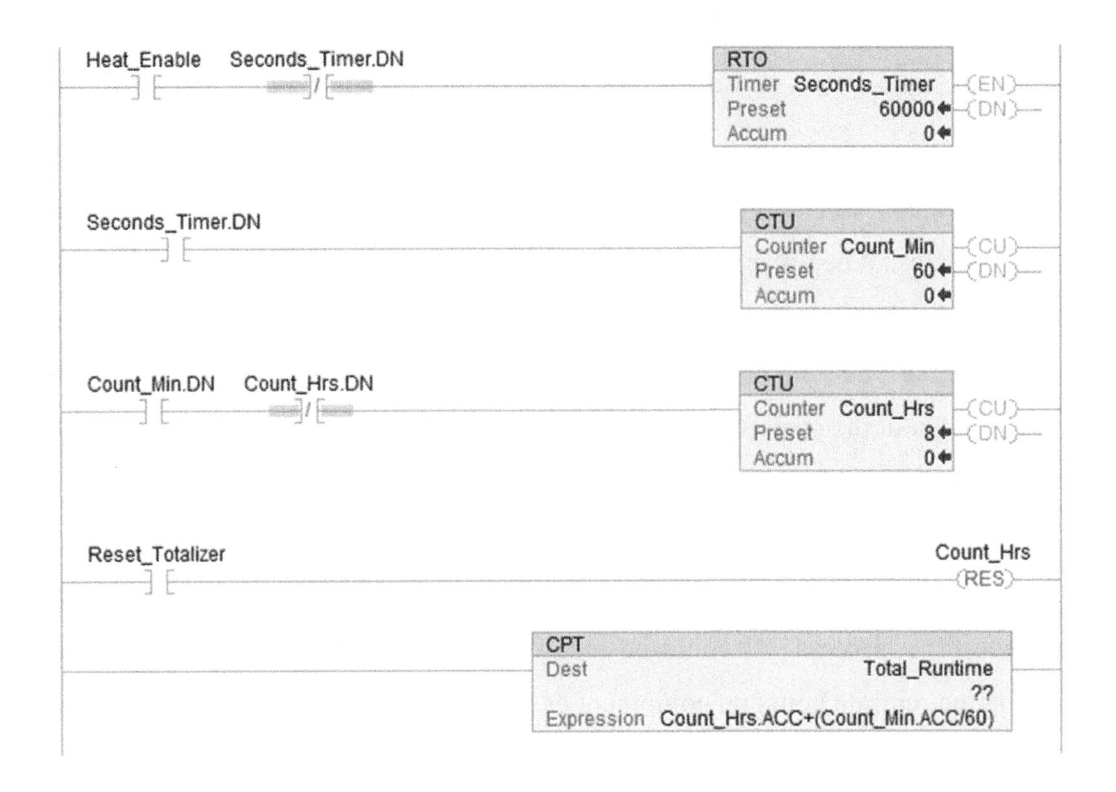

The length of an AOI is immaterial to our discussion at this point – I've seen some that were quite complex and used many instructions, and some that are only a single rung in length. The essential thing to understand, where AOI's are concerned, is that they are used to solve specific problems, and provide a function similar to that of a subroutine. I've seen AOI's used in a variety of applications. For example; performing mass-flow math calculations for burner controls, scaling for analog values, utilized with motor control, and performing data communications transfer on the initial start-up of equipment. One way of thinking about AOI's, is that they provide a basic construct similar to a user-defined data type (UDT), but include user-designed logic programming as well. In addition, they can be used in numerous instances throughout a project, or exported to another project.

CREATING THE RUNTIME AOI:

Here are the basic steps in creating an AOI. To get started simply go to the Project Organizer, right-click the Add-On Instructions folder and select "New Add-On Instruction".

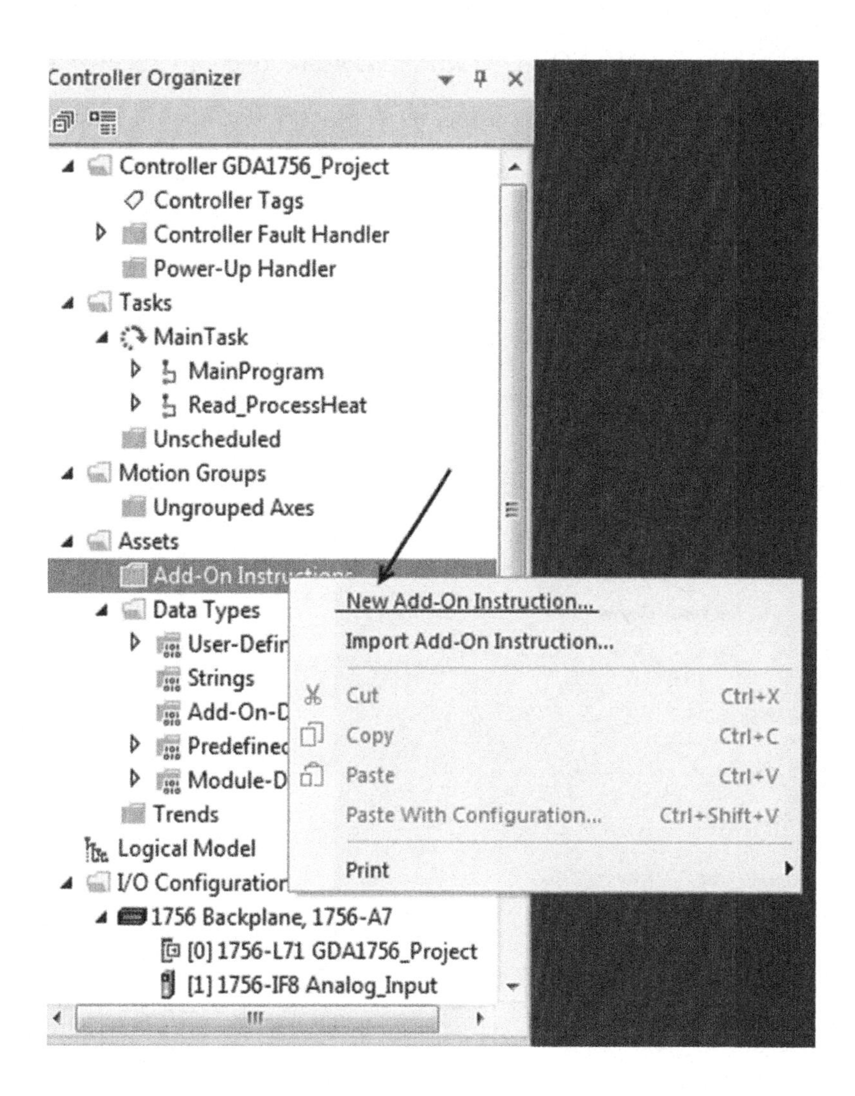

At this point the New Add-On Instruction menu opens, where you can give the AOI a name, short description, and set a revision number if desired.

Once you click the [OK] tab, the Add-On Definition menu opens. From this menu, you'll be able to add and define the *parameters* and *local tags* that will be used in the AOI logic.

There are four types of parameters can be defined and used; *Input, Output, In/Out,* and *Public*. Of these four, Input, Output, and occasionally the In/Out parameter types have the greatest applicability with AOI's. *Parameters* are used to receive or pass data between the finished AOI and the routine it is placed within. *Local Tags* operate differently, in that they only function within the AOI, they do not pass data or signals outside of the AOI.

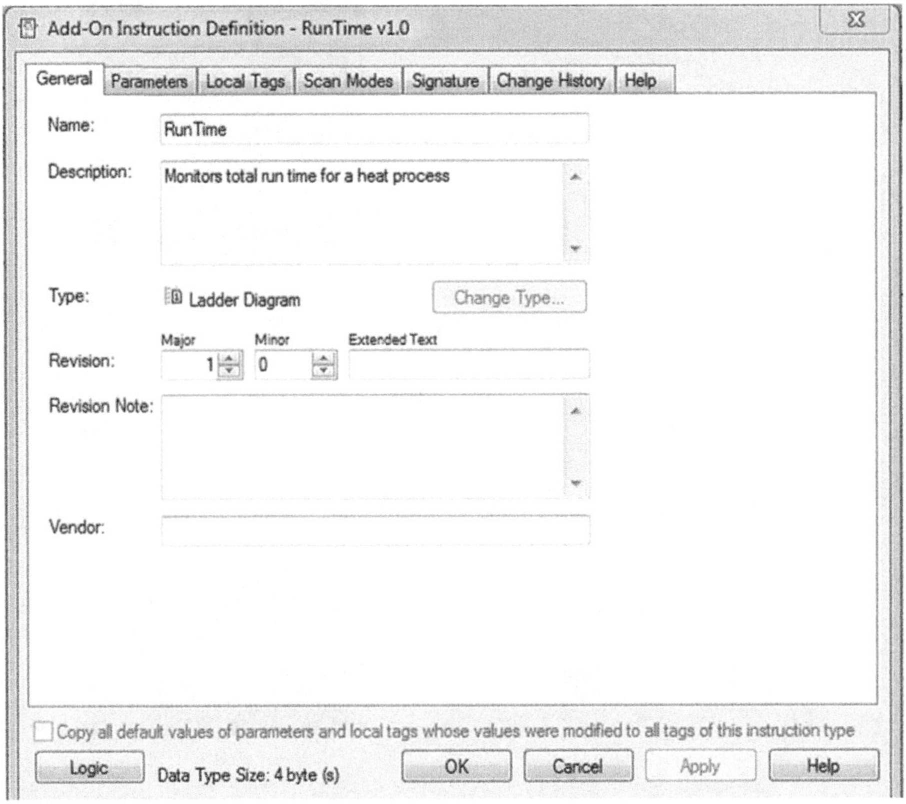

Select the *Parameters* tab and enter the Tag names for the inputs and outputs required by the instruction. This of course, is determined by what you want the AOI to accomplish. From this menu, you also choose which items will be visible on the instruction and which items will be required. Any Tag checked as "required" will also be visible in the instruction block. For this example, the parameters *Heat_Enable* and *Total_Runtime* are required and selected to be visible within the instruction block.

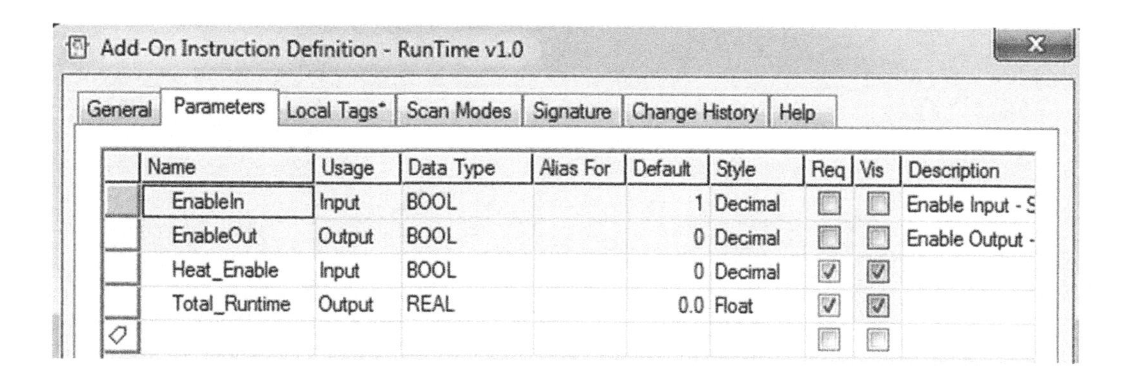

Add-On Instruction Definition - RunTime v1.0

General | Parameters | Local Tags* | Scan Modes | Signature | Change History | Help

Name	Usage	Data Type	Alias For	Default	Style	Req	Vis	Description
EnableIn	Input	BOOL		1	Decimal	☐	☐	Enable Input - S
EnableOut	Output	BOOL		0	Decimal	☐	☐	Enable Output -
Heat_Enable	Input	BOOL		0	Decimal	☑	☑	
Total_Runtime	Output	REAL		0.0	Float	☑	☑	
						☐	☐	

Next we'll select the Local Tags tab and make entries for our counters and a timer. Note that all of these items, both parameters and local tags, must be defined by an appropriate data-type, just the same as any other tag you would create.

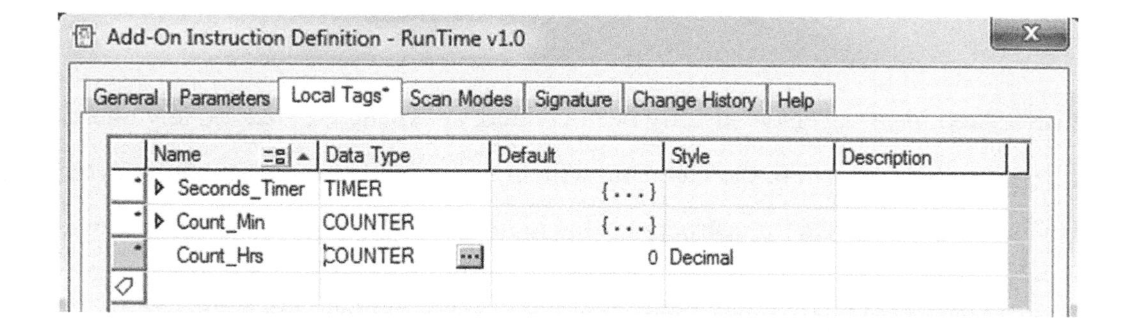

Add-On Instruction Definition - RunTime v1.0

General | Parameters | Local Tags* | Scan Modes | Signature | Change History | Help

Name	Data Type	Default	Style	Description
Seconds_Timer	TIMER	{...}		
Count_Min	COUNTER	{...}		
Count_Hrs	COUNTER	0	Decimal	

CREATING THE AOI LOGIC:

When finished defining parameters and local tags, click on [Apply] and [OK], and begin the logic for the RunTime AOI. At this point, you can go ahead and create the program structure, which is what I've done here, adding the defined tags afterward – or just build it rung-by-rung.

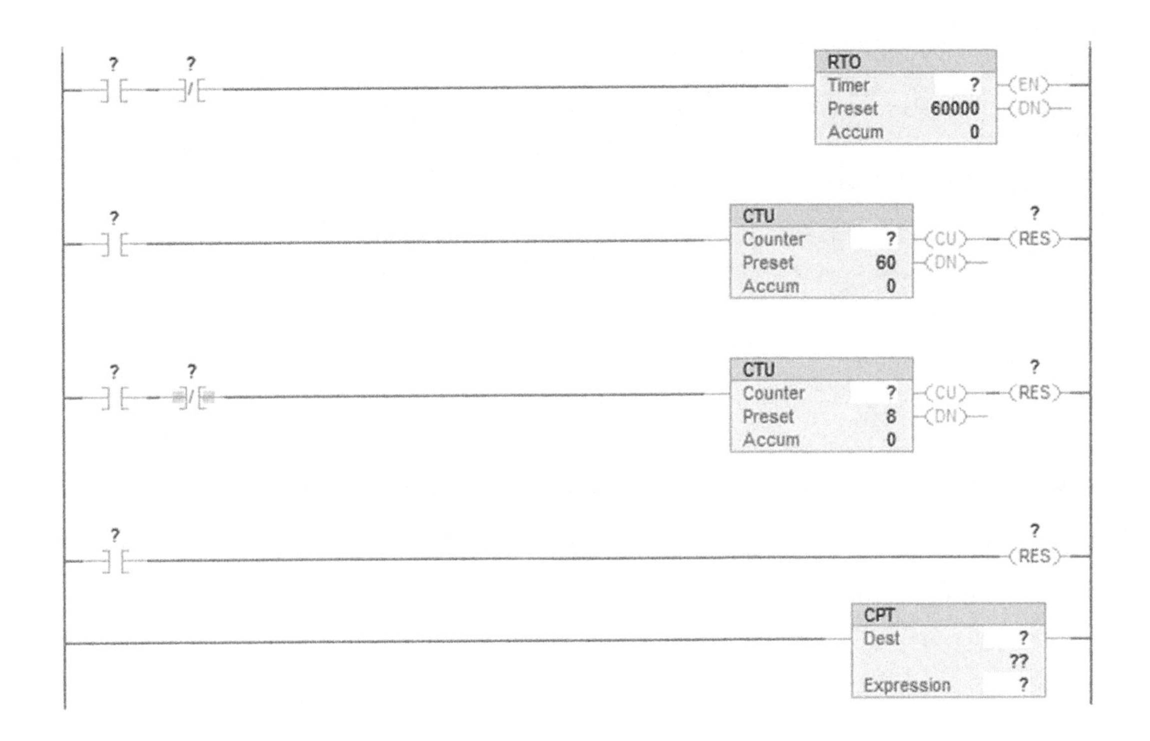

Parameters and local tags have already been created, so when you click on any question mark **[?]** on the instruction, the elements will show in the drop down menu for you to select. After selecting tags for instructions, the logic should look similar to the following:

Finally, select the Add-On Instruction, now located on the instructions bar under "Add-On", and place it within the routine where needed. It can be used for multiple processes: P1, P2, P3 …, and could be used in different routines as well.

In the following example, you see the new AOI as it would appear in the ladder program as a *single instruction block* called "RunTime".

RunTime
RunTime ??
Heat_Enable ??
Total_Runtime ??
Reset_Totalizer ??

Whenever rung conditions allow, it will run its specific logic, and provide a calculated value in the destination tag named *Total_Runtime*.

For every *instance* where the *RunTime* AOI is used, data is pulled from *Total_Runtime* parameter and placed into a tag that you create and is unique to that process, such as *Runtime_Process_1*, or *Runtime_Process_3*.

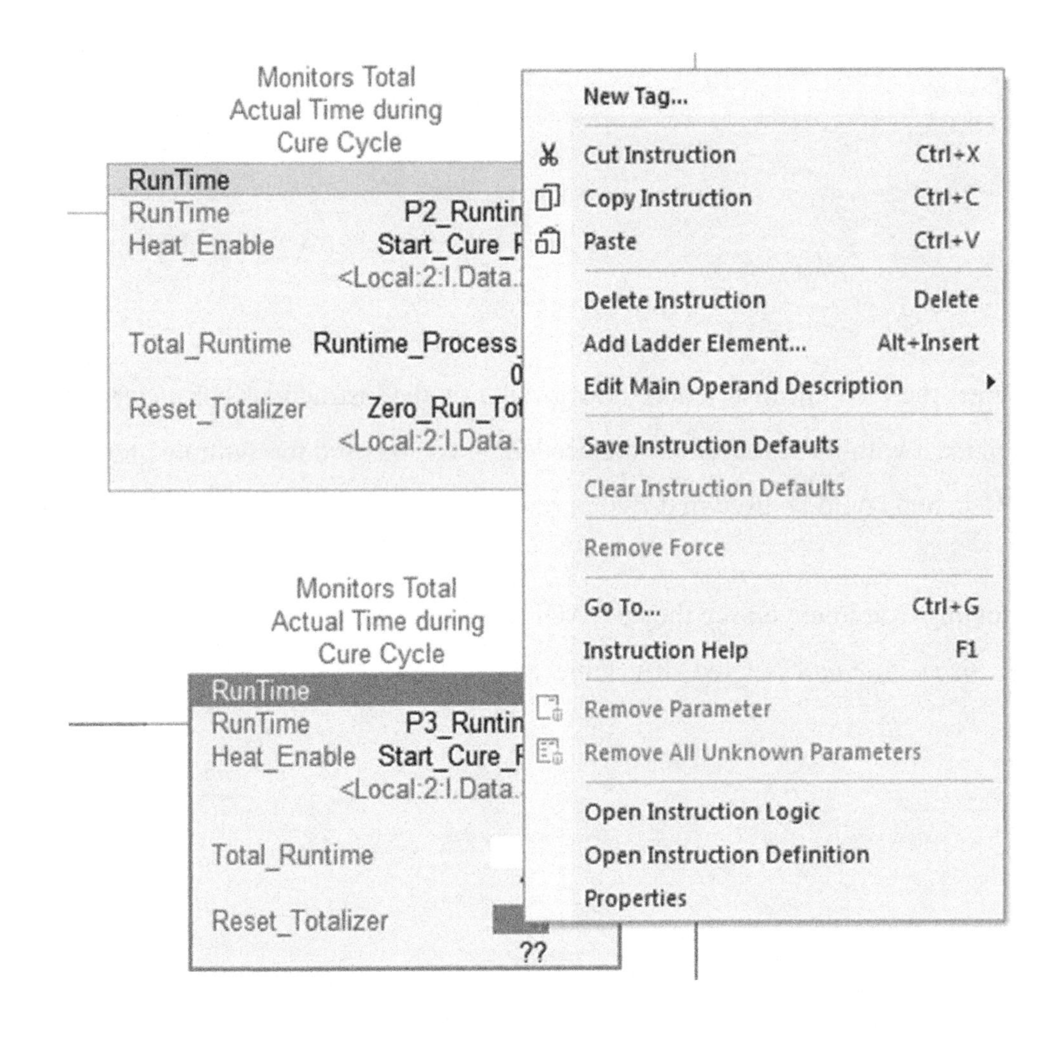

Name the AOI *instance* by selecting the "New Tag" option, in this example **P3_Runtime.** Do the same for the **Heat_Enable** and **Reset_Totalizer** inputs, and the **Total_Runtime** output – giving them an "alias" name and selecting the desired input or output data point or tag. These alias tags must be created before they can be used within the instruction.

Note that the RunTime names; **P1_Runtime** and **P2_Runtime** are simply names I've given using the "New Tag" option. The other tag names; **Start_Cure_P1**, **Start_Cure_P2**, **Runtime_Process_1**, **Runtime_Process_2**, and the **Zero_Run_Total** tags, are all *alias's* given for specific memory allocations, which will pass data or signals, to or from the input and output parameters designated as we created the AOI.

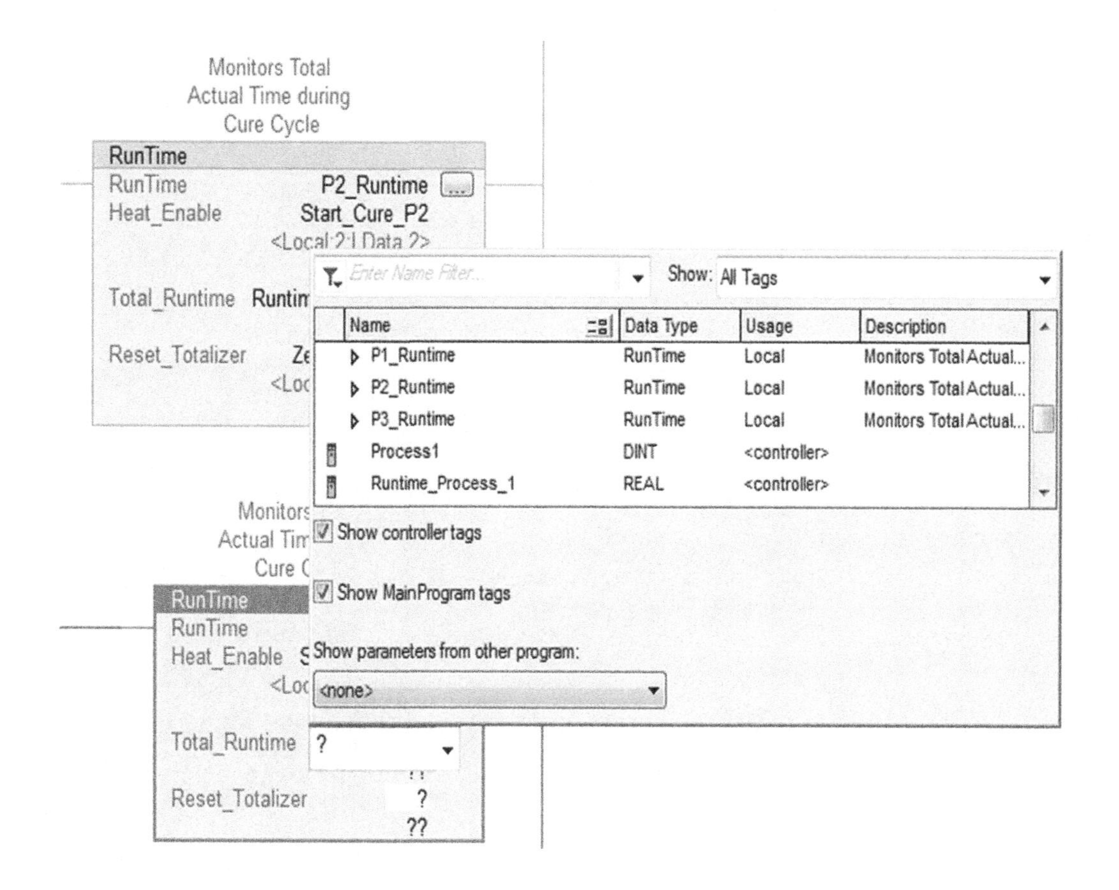

As you can see, this provides a means for having multiple instances of using this AOI within the same routine or other routines. Select "Data Context" from the top display bar to see the instances where your AOI has been placed.

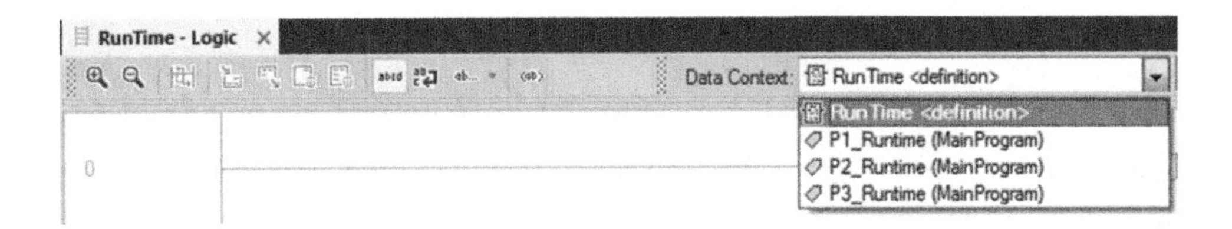

Finally, the finished AOI placed in a routine and used to track run time for Process 1 and Process 2. There are many other types of repetitive programming tasks where AOI's can be used.

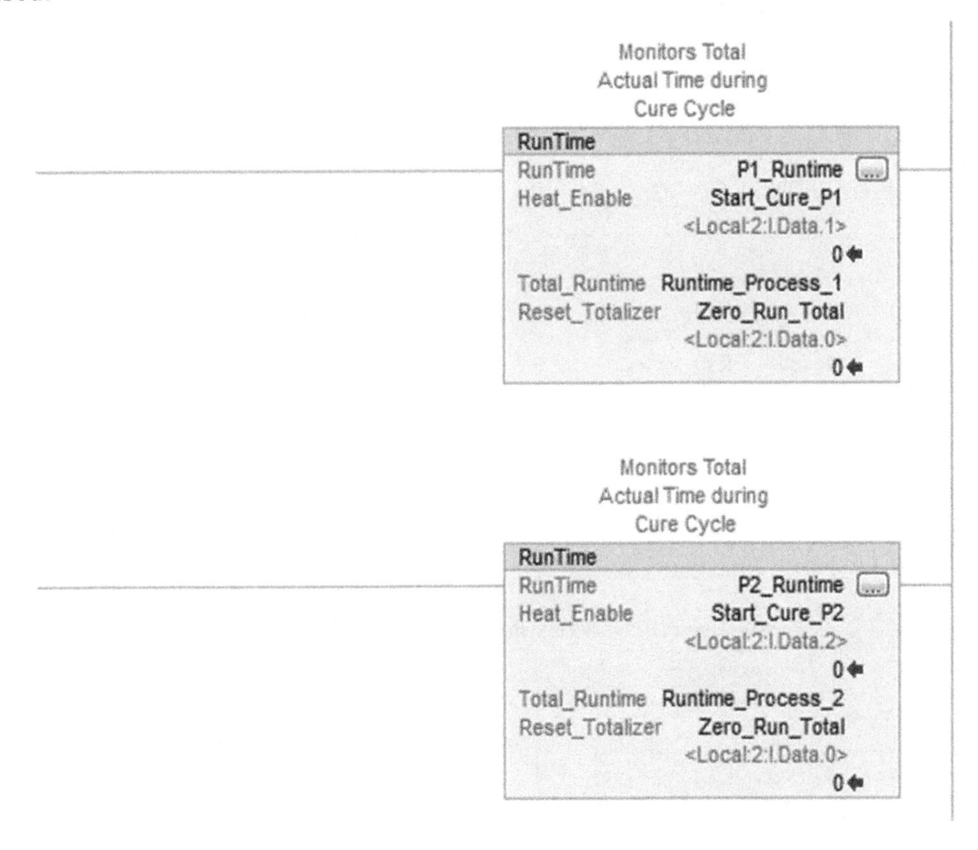

Steps for creating an Add-On Instruction:

1. Right-click on the Add-*On Instruction* folder in the Project Organizer, then select *New Add-On Instruction*.

2. Give your instruction a name, description and the type of programming that will be used to build it.

3. Consider and select which attributes – inputs and output tags are required and which will need to be visible in the instruction block.

4. Open the *Definition* menu to enter needed parameters and local tags. Input parameters for receiving an input from outside the AOI. Output parameters for containing a result of the AOI logic that can be sent or passed back into the parent routine. In/Out parameters are used as a reference to data from outside the AOI, and function similar to an alias tag for input or output that can be used by the AOI. Local tags are for instruction operands or tags used only within the AOI and not passed outside of the AOI.

5. Double-click on the logic routine in the Project Organizer and create the logic. Use normal addressing conventions; Method 1 or Method 2 to select parameter names and local tags for your created logic.

6. Use the instruction with needed routines. Remember that tags you will assign, must be created before they can be used within the instruction. Create these tags in the Controller Tags or Program Tags section.

For Reference see PUB 1756-PM010 and PUB 1756-PM021

Hands-On Exercise

In this exercise, spend some time building an Add-On Instruction (AOI) that could be used to start, stop, and monitor various sections of a conveyor system. Here is sample logic to use for this exercise – but create your own if you wish:

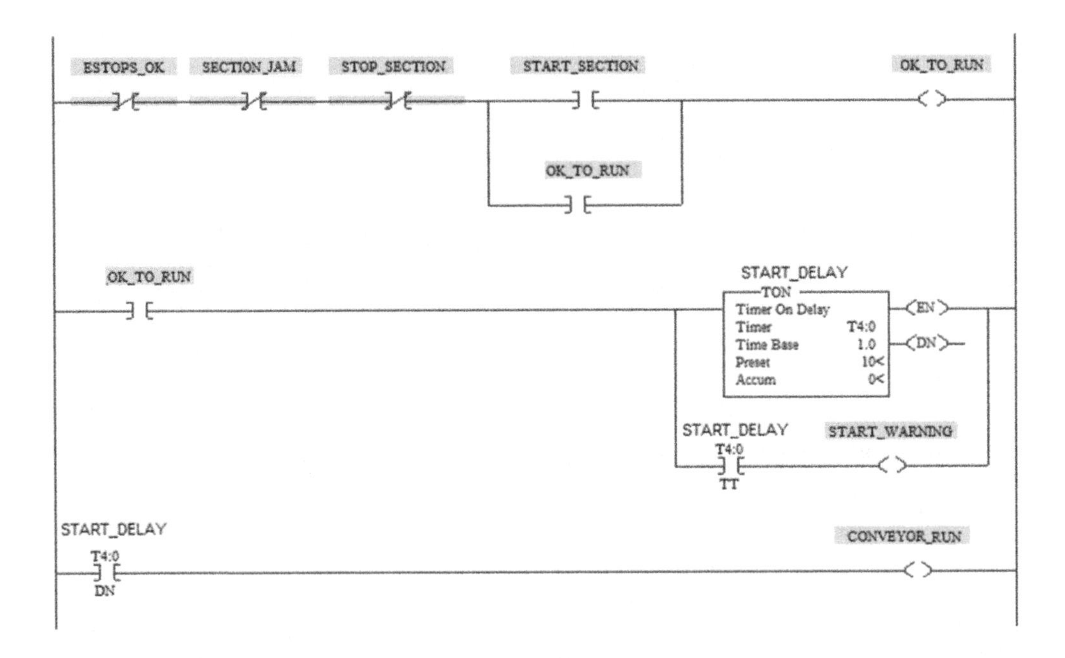

1. Add the AOI – using the New Add-On Instruction selection

2. Define AOI *Parameters* and the *Local tags* for the example logic. Note that the above input and output parameters are "general", and so will be linked to alias tags which can be unique to each instance where they are used. For example; Conveyor1, Conveyor2, or Conveyor3…all having different physical I/O for their Starts, Stops, Conveyor_Run, and Start_Warning alarms.

3. Use the newly created AOI in one of the routines for two or more conveyor sections, creating the alias tags and associating the inputs and outputs with the appropriate I/O points.

4. Are the parameters and linked I/O points visible in your completed instruction block?

CREATING AND USING ARRAYS:

An array is a method of using blocks of memory for data of the same data type. Normally, arrays are used to provide logical grouping for data items that performs a similar function. When creating an array, you configure a block of memory that can utilize one, two, or three dimensions to accommodate the data. The rule for designating a tag as an array, is to add a subscript value(s) after the data type that represents the dimensional [x, y, z] values. For instance; DINT[6] for a 6 element, 32 bits each – one dimensional array, DINT[10,10] for a 100 element, two dimensional array, or a DINT[3,3,4] for a 36 element, three dimensional array.

Here is an example of a simple one-dimensional array of DINT[6]. To create the array, create a tag by clicking on the Controller Tags folder, and then selecting the Tag Editor. Select the scope of the tag, controller or program, and then type the name of the new tag into the open name field at the bottom of the list. Next, enter the data type and dimensions, with the number of elements set off in brackets as the subscript.

− Preset_Value		{...}	{...}	Decimal	DINT[6]
+ Preset_Value[0]		25000		Decimal	DINT
+ Preset_Value[1]		50000		Decimal	DINT
+ Preset_Value[2]		75000		Decimal	DINT
+ Preset_Value[3]		100000		Decimal	DINT
+ Preset_Value[4]		125000		Decimal	DINT
+ Preset_Value[5]		150000		Decimal	DINT

In an array, each data location is an element in a contiguous block of memory; therefore each element is located in sequence. Note that in this example of the **Preset_Value** array, that each individual array element contains 32 bits if expanded. This makes it possible to use array and sequencing instructions when working with array data values in program logic. It also allows an array to be a valuable tool to use with equipment or processes that use the same programming - but with different values. An example of this might be multiple recipes accommodating different parts in a curing oven or autoclave process, each having different cure times, heat rates, or pressure settings.

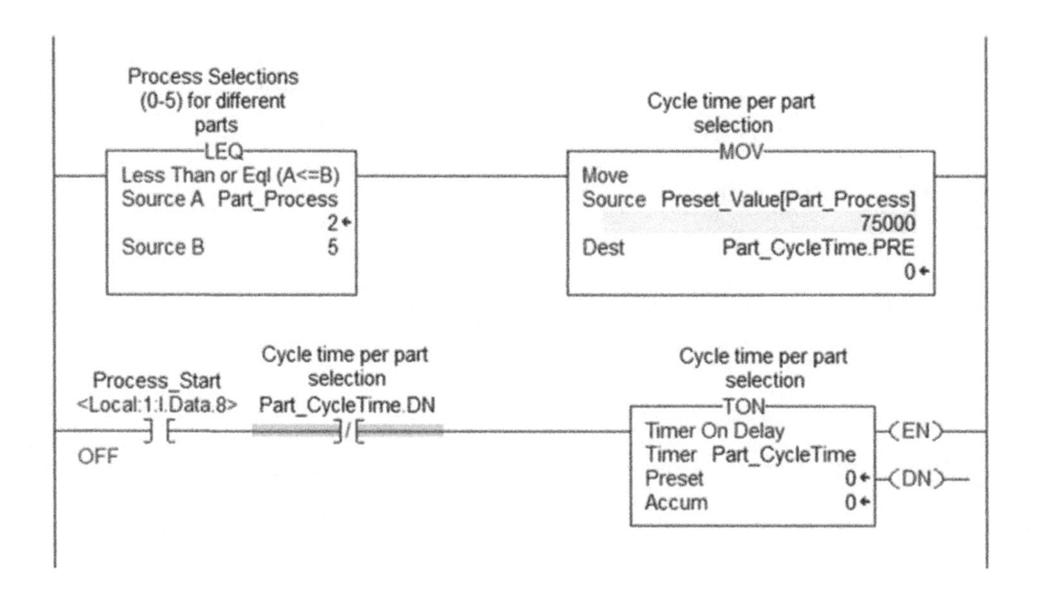

Using the **Preset_Value** array shows how a timer can be updated with different preset values depending on which part has been selected for processing. In this example, I've set the Preset_Value array with different values (constants) that will be placed into the **Part_CycleTime** timer preset – dependent upon the **Part_Process** selection. There are numerous other things that could be done here; these preset values could be moved into the array elements by another program, or each of these elements could be used on multiple timers. There are a lot of options and opportunities for the creative use of an array.

In the following logic example, if the selection is qualified by the LEQ instruction, the preset value for the specific part selection is moved into the preset of the timer. Once *Process_Start* is initiated by operator or program, the timer begins its timing cycle. This type of program logic could also be used when the overall process requires timed values for different segments, each having different requirements that might pertain to heating, pressures or other variables. The timer could be cycled through all of the preset values by using an ADD instruction and adding the number 1 (indexing) to the next Part-Process value for the MOV instruction source.

Care must be taken when indexing values in this fashion. Anytime a subscript becomes out-of-range, exceeding the number of elements in the array, it will cause a major fault code (4,20) on the controller. This type of fault can be cleared by a fault routine – which will be discussed in a later section, but it is still the best practice to avoid out-of-range subscripts by correct programming. Just as a tag can be defined by a user-defined data type (UDT), a tag which is designated as an array can be used within a UDT as well. This is useful, as in the preceding example, when there are multiple recipes or part processes that each require the same data elements but with different values.

In the example that follows, I've built a UDT which is named FAULTS_MAJOR. This UDT will be used to illustrate a method of obtaining fault information in a later chapter, but for now just serves the purpose of showing how one member of the (UDT) requires a larger block of memory. To accommodate this need, an array defined as a DINT[8] is placed within the UDT for the *Fault_Info* member.

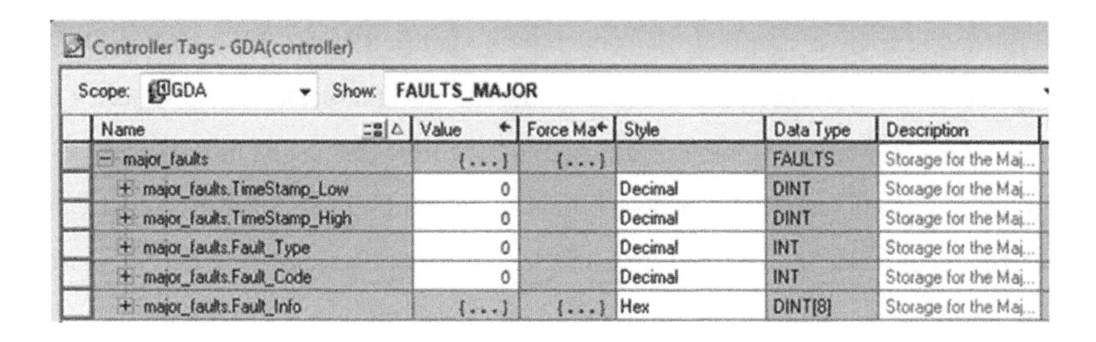
Controller Tags - GDA(controller)

Scope: GDA Show: FAULTS_MAJOR

Name	Value	Force Mask	Style	Data Type	Description
− major_faults	{...}	{...}		FAULTS	Storage for the Maj...
+ major_faults.TimeStamp_Low	0		Decimal	DINT	Storage for the Maj...
+ major_faults.TimeStamp_High	0		Decimal	DINT	Storage for the Maj...
+ major_faults.Fault_Type	0		Decimal	INT	Storage for the Maj...
+ major_faults.Fault_Code	0		Decimal	INT	Storage for the Maj...
+ major_faults.Fault_Info	{...}	{...}	Hex	DINT[8]	Storage for the Maj...

There are many specialized instructions that are particularly useful when working with the data contained in an array. Here are several "file" type instructions:

- FAL – File Arithmetic and Logic instruction.
- FSC – File Search & Compare instruction
- FLL – File Fill instruction
- COP – Copy File instruction
- CPS – Synchronous Copy File instruction
- AVE – Average the array elements instruction
- STD – Standard Deviation of array elements instruction
- SIZE – Array size instruction

For a complete list and descriptions of these and many other instructions that work when using arrays, see reference PUB 1756-RM003R.

THE NEED FOR BUFFERING:

The use of asynchronous scanning in the ControlLogix platform, even though efficient, powerful, and fast, has created the need for some different programming techniques. One such need is to buffer the inputs and outputs of I/O modules. This problem area is created by the very different method in which a ControlLogix controller handles the solving of logic, as it relates to updated values of input and output module tags.

Remember in the world of legacy PLC's the scan cycle was "synchronous". Essentially, all the different duties performed by the controller were accomplished during the same cycle-of-time with each function having a section of that time cycle. Each function was performed sequentially until the scan completed and began again – repeating the same cycle. Here again is a simple illustration of that type of scan cycle.

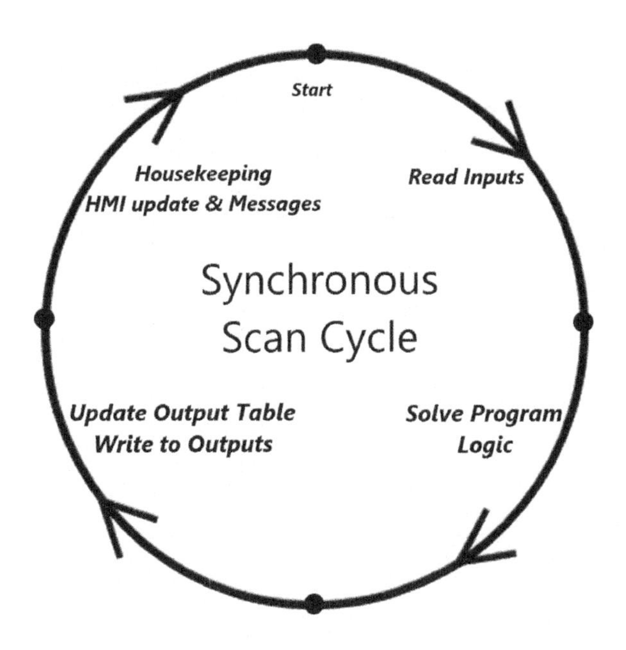

After the processor scanned inputs and updated the input data table, it moved into the next phase of executing program logic. Once the processor moves into the logic-solving phase, it didn't really matter if physical inputs changed their state – the input table had already been updated and those were the values now used in solving the program logic. Any changes in physical inputs would be picked up on the next scan. Basically, as far as the input table was concerned, the state of an input could never change_during the point of the scan-cycle when program execution was occurring. This is not the case however, when the controller employs asynchronous scanning.

Recall that with asynchronous scanning, the inputs, outputs, program execution, and housekeeping functions are all occurring *independently* rather than in any sequential order that would remotely resemble a synchronous scan cycle. Here is a simple illustration showing the independent scans for each of these primary functions in a ControlLogix controller.

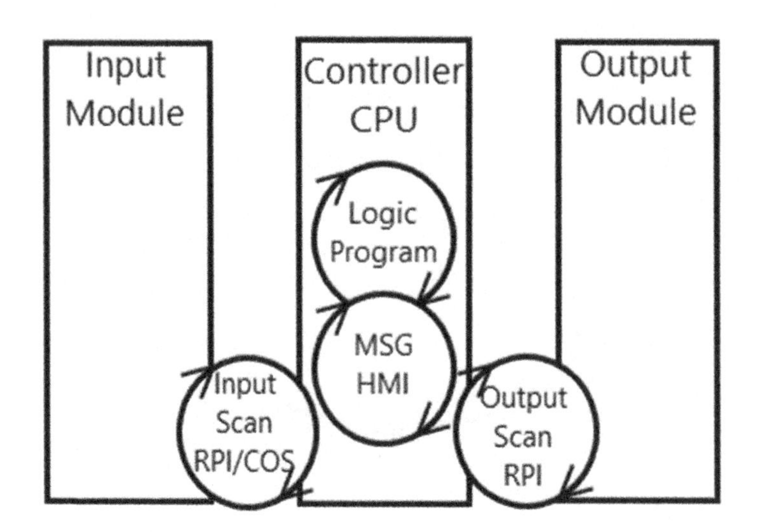

With this type of scanning, it is not only possible for input values to change, but also for their changing state to be reflected in the program's logic during execution. This can create numerous problems unless corrected. We must handle inputs and outputs in a way that prevents rapidly changing states from directly affecting the program logic. Here is an example, showing how this type of problem can occur if we fail to buffer the I/O points in our project *before* executing the logic routine that uses them.

In this hypothetical example, the input module is set to send data every 25 ms, whereas the logic scan requires twice that amount of time, approximately 50 ms. Since input data would be sent to the processor twice during a single logic scan, this creates the possibility for the FT1 input to be in one state during the first half-scan of program logic and then change to the opposite state during the second half of program execution.

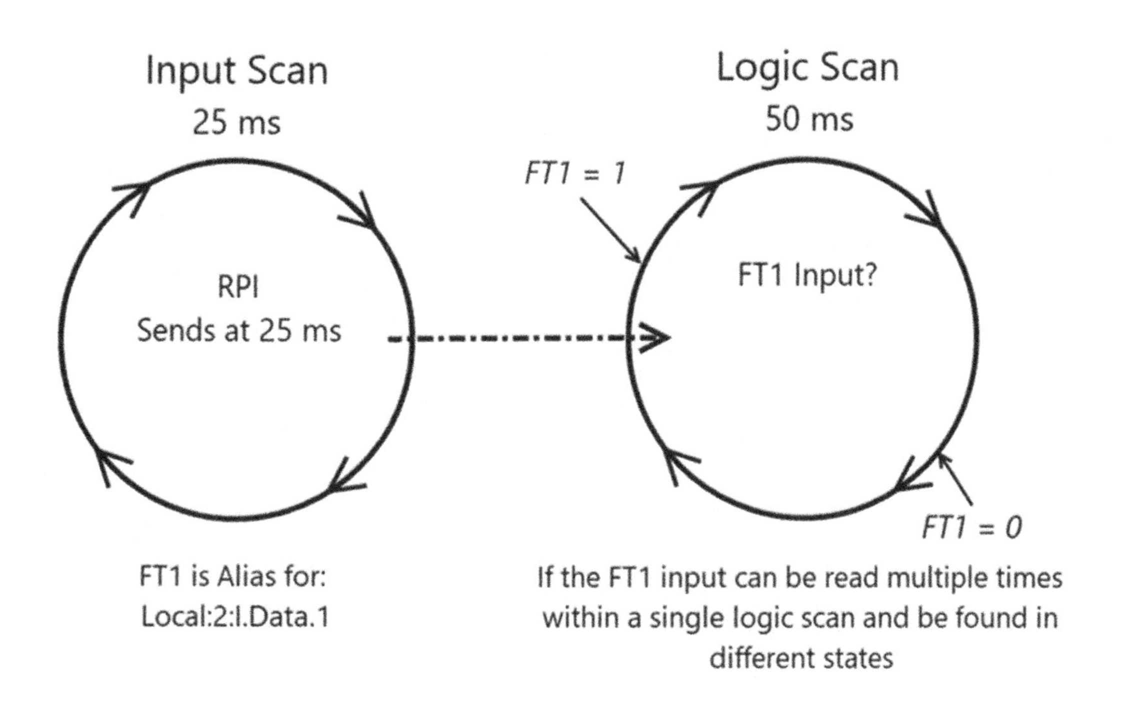

By buffering the input, we *capture the state* of FT1 in an *internal memory allocation before* executing the routine that directly uses it. The internal memory retains the current state, even if the physical input does not, until the buffer (mapping) routine is executed again. Remember, in the ControlLogix platform, programs are called and routines executed in a definite order. This is one of the characteristics of ControlLogix which can be used to create the routines necessary to capture the current state of input values, call the routines necessary to solve control logic for equipment or a process, and then buffer our output values to actually perform the control operations.

BUFFERING I/O DATA:

One of the primary methods of buffering input and output values is by using base tags. This is also often referred to as *mapping*. There are a couple of ways to do this; one is to create base tags in memory designated as a BOOL data type, and then use these tags in a logic routine that will capture input values. The other is essentially the same except for designating the base tags as a double-integer (DINT) data type. This second method is a more efficient use of memory and easy to do, so I'll show both methods in the examples that follow. Buffering output values is essentially the same process in reverse – as output buffer tags are copied or moved to actual output tags.

While I/O buffering can be programmed and successfully accomplished in several different ways, it usually involves the use of three types of routines – which are called and executed in a definite order by the active program. This type of programming tends to be less confusing because it maintains some degree of separation between the functions of each routine. The addition of thoughtful tag-names and descriptions are always helpful as well. Once again, the goal of buffering is to *capture* the state of an input which may be subjected to rapid changes, into an internal buffer-tag which will not change - until the input-mapping routine is once again executed. After the input mapping routine runs, the process routine uses the buffer-tags in solving program logic. So the three basic routines for buffering are:

- First – the routine that maps the current state of inputs.
- Second – the routine that controls our process and equipment.
- Third – a routine that maps output values to the output table for a module.

Here is a screenshot of the MainRoutine in a program. In the Controller organizer you can see the other subroutines I've created for this example. Remember that each routine is created within the project by doing a right-click on **MainProgram** and selecting the "New Routine" option. The routines created will all fall under the MainProgram heading in alphabetical order – not the order in which they will execute.

MainRoutine & Buffering

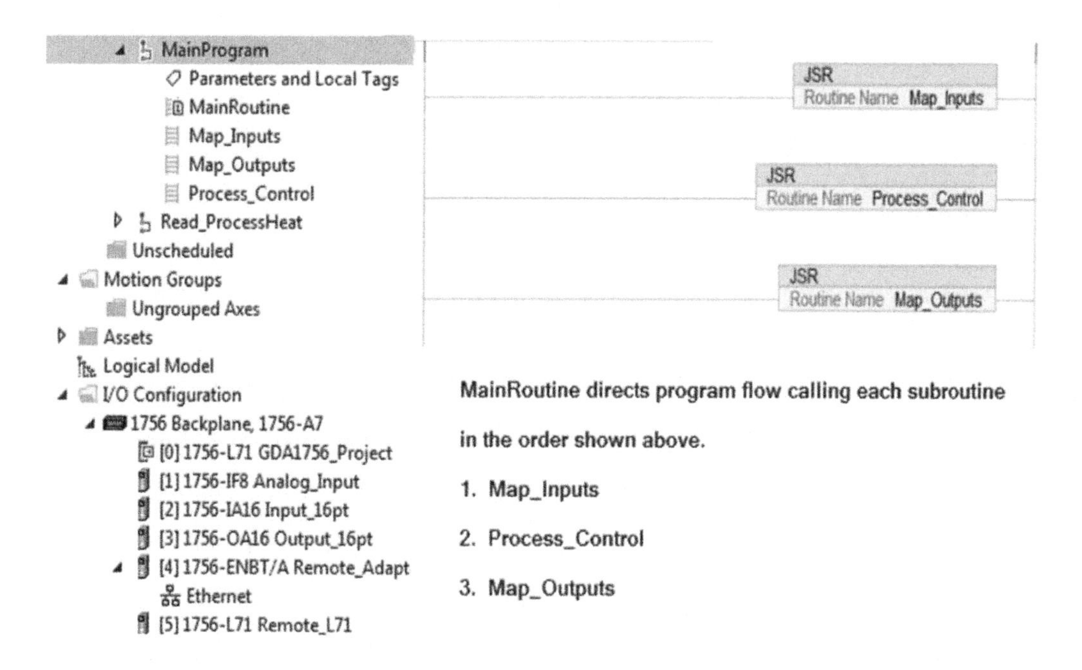

Remember from previous discussion, that the MainRoutine (in any given program) determines *when* other routines in the program are called and executed. So, except for the possible interruption of a periodic task, these three routines will execute in the order directed by the *jump-to-subroutine* (JSR) instructions.

Going first to the *Map_Inputs* routine, I've created the following ladder logic. For simplicity, I've only shown the first four data input points on the module, but you would normally create these rungs for all of the module's inputs – along with the buffer tags. These buffer tags can then be used multiple times throughout the logic program.

Map_Inputs Routine

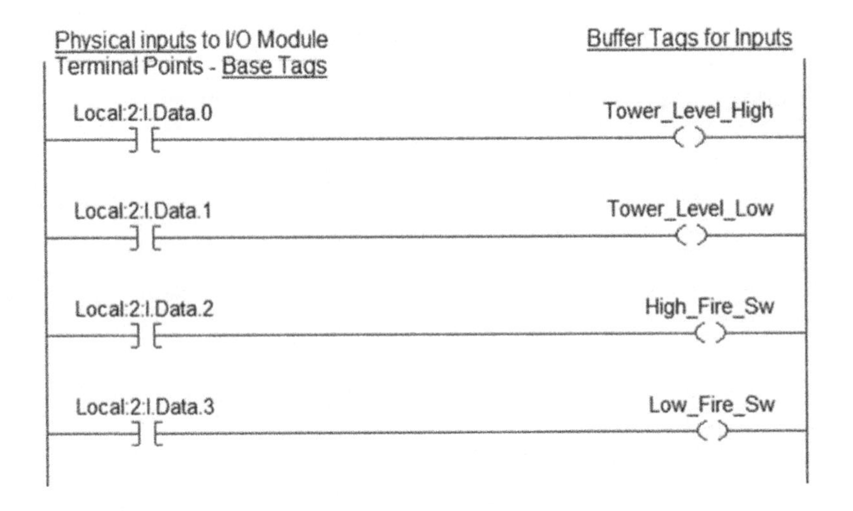

As you can see from this, there isn't any need to assign an alias to these base input tags since this is the only time they are directly used in a program routine. Also, their functions are apparent by the names used for their respective buffer tags, which are how the inputs will be referenced and used in other logic routines, by their buffer tag-names. Each buffer tag is named and defined as a BOOL data type by first doing a right-click on the question-mark **[?]** above the newly placed (OTE) instruction, and then selecting the *New Tag*

option. This is the same process we used earlier to create tags during the ladder programming process.

This next example does the very same thing; map the inputs to buffer tags, but does so by using a slightly different method. Here we define a DINT data type, a full 32 bits, with buffer tag-names. I've used the name I02.0, I02.1, I02.2 … etc., to indicate *Input, Slot 2* and the *data-point*, until we've utilized the full 16 data points of our input module. Each name is defined down to bit level since we have designated this as a DINT, rather than the BOOL, data type. With this method, *description* becomes an important identifier. As you right-click on the name of each OTE instruction, one of the options given is "*Edit the Main Operand Description*". By doing this, descriptive text, such as *Tower Level High* or *High Fire Switch*, can be added for each input buffer tag and will appear in all logic routines along with the tag name.

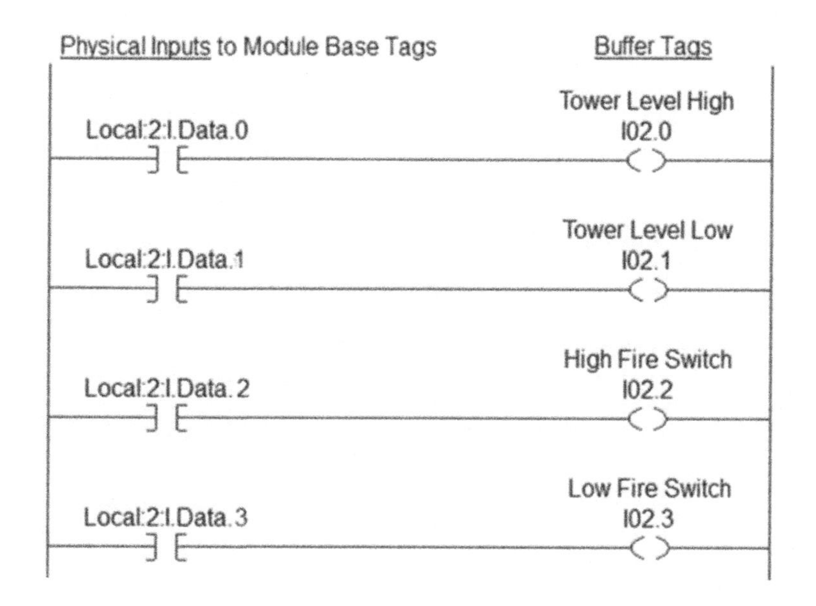

After the *Map_Inputs* routine has ran, *MainRoutine* calls for the next routine in its logic sequence to execute. I've named this routine *Process_Control,* it being the logic or programming that provides functional control for the equipment or process.

In these few rungs, we're updating some status and alarm indicators by using the buffered tags from the previous input mapping routine.

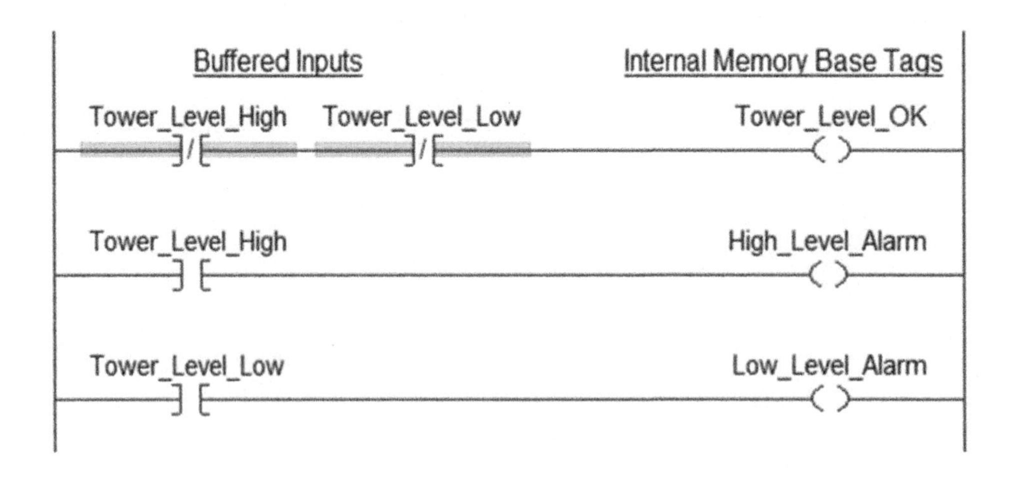

The last subroutine to be called is the *Map Outputs* routine. It simply takes the values in internal memory allocations that have been solved in the *Process_Control* routine, and updates the actual output tags for the output module in our ControlLogix chassis, the module itself is updated per its configured RPI setting.

Map_Outputs Routine

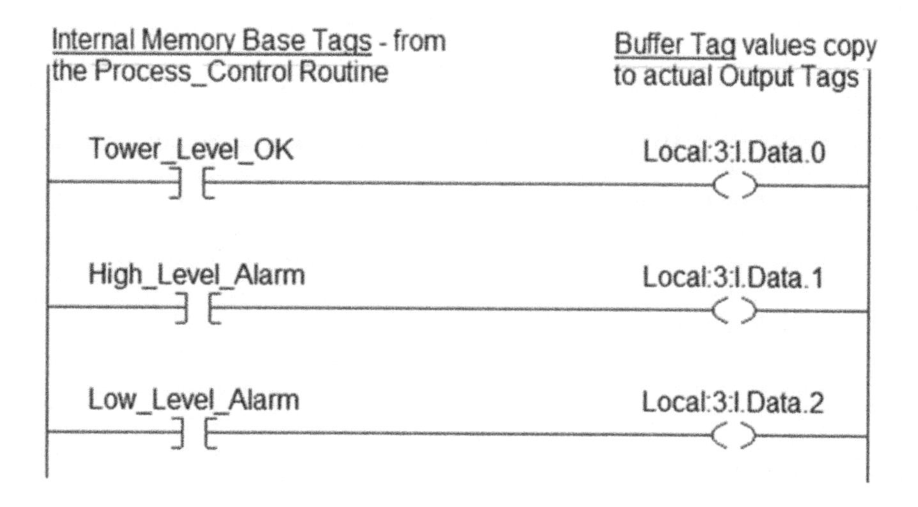

This completes all three types of routines needed to buffer I/O terminal points. I think one of the main values of this last routine, is that it clearly shows tag-name associations, and how they carry through from our input logic to the actual outputs.

An obvious fact is that physical outputs aren't really subject to the same dynamics as physical inputs, they only change as a result of solved logic, so one might ask why even bother in using a separate routine like the one just shown. That said, it would probably be acceptable to assign alias tag-names for outpoint points and use these aliases directly in the functional routine – *Process_Control*, as long as they were used *only once* in the logic. But then this gets back to why buffering is necessary in the first place – to prevent an input or output from being in one state early in the program logic, and in another state later in the logic scan. Buffering outputs, as well as the inputs, puts this issue to rest and allows more flexibility in using the buffered output tags multiple times in the logic routine.

Using Parameters to Buffer I/O Data:

One additional method of buffering I/O points is by the use of parameters. This is only available when using versions 24 and higher of the RSLogix 5000 software. When using these versions of Logix Designer software to build a project, you are able to create associations between input or output tags that have dynamic values, and program parameters. The benefit of this, is that parameters are automatically buffered at a *specific time* during the logic scan, and so will not be changed during the execution of the program.

Here again, is the illustration of asynchronous processing taking place in a ControlLogix controller. As shown by the arrowed circles, these cycles are independent of one another – so while input values may be rapidly changing, this doesn't affect any immediate change to their value or status within the logic scan-cycle.

Asynchronous Scans of ControlLogix Controller

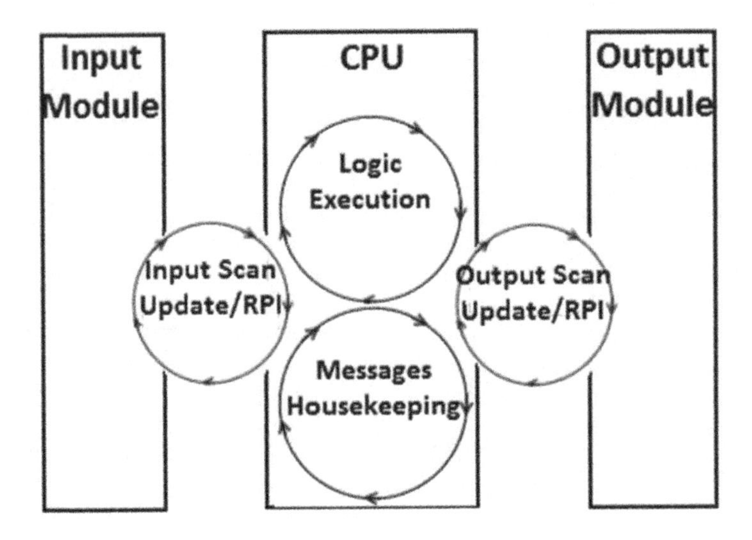

Of the four parameter types for use in programs, two types: the Input and Output types are best suited to for buffering I/O module data points. The Input type of parameter receives an update at the beginning of the logic scan. The output type of parameter receives an update at the end of the logic scan.

To create an association between a desired tag and parameter; start by double-clicking on the *Parameters and Local Tags* folder located under a Program heading in the Controller Organizer pane. Note that this has replaced the *Program Tags* folder that was standard in earlier versions. Once you have selected *New Parameter* from the options menu you can fill in the other details necessary to create the parameter/tag link.

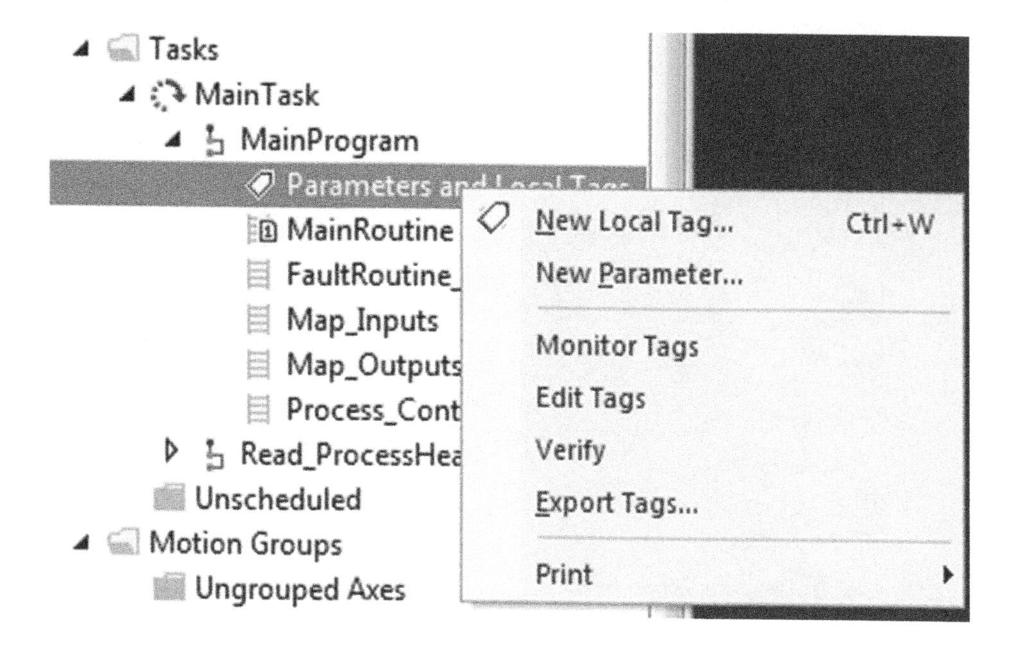

From here, you give the parameter a name – this is the base tag name which you can use directly in ladder routines. Select the *Parameter Connections* option to select the data point (input or output), and other relevant details such as description, scope, data type, and style.

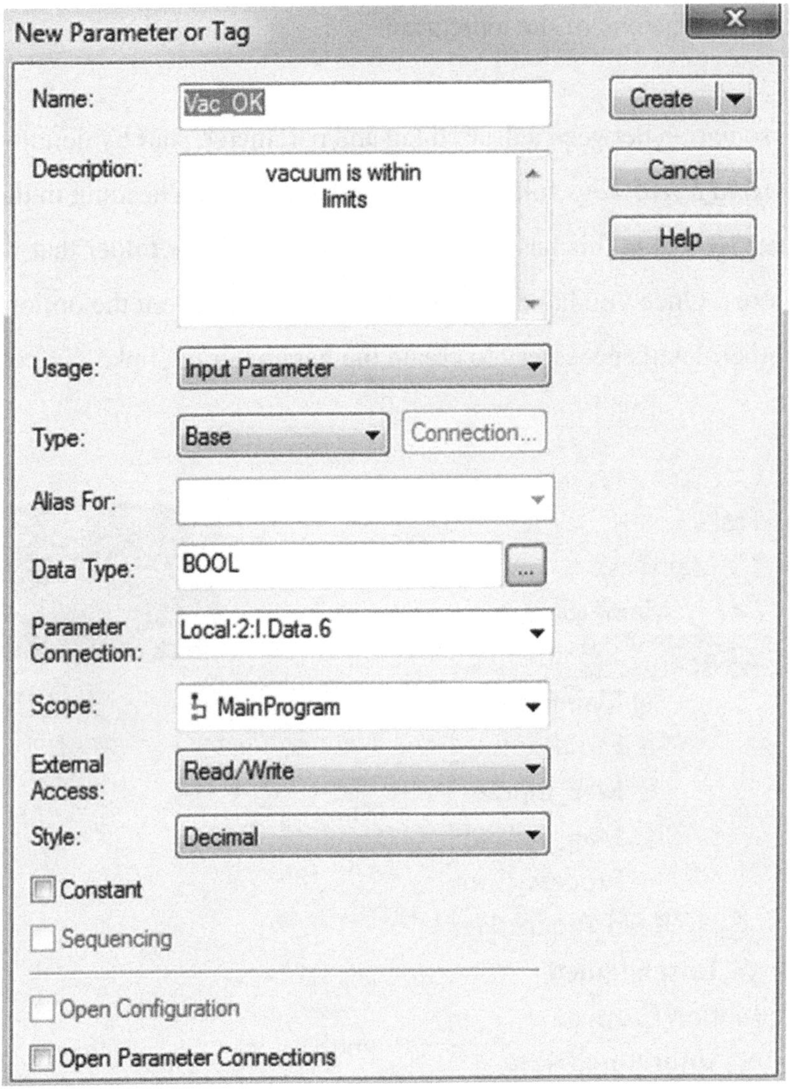

New Parameter or Tag

Name: Vac_OK

Description: vacuum is within limits

Usage: Input Parameter

Type: Base | Connection...

Alias For:

Data Type: BOOL

Parameter Connection: Local:2:I.Data.6

Scope: MainProgram

External Access: Read/Write

Style: Decimal

Constant

Sequencing

Open Configuration

Open Parameter Connections

Create | Cancel | Help

As you use the parameter tag in various ladder routines, remember that parameters are updated at specific times during the logic scan. The new parameter tag shown in this example; **Vac_OK**, is updated at the beginning of the logic scan, and remains in this state throughout the scan, regardless if its associated input changes.

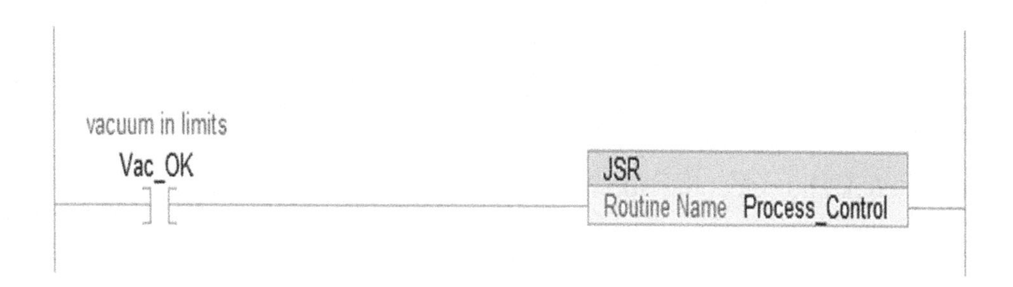

Output parameters are updated at the end of the program scan. So parameters buffer I/O due to the fact that they are not updated during the execution of the program logic.

For more information on Buffering I/O and the use of parameters, see the following Rockwell Automation publications in the literature library:

PUB 1756-PM004F-EN-P, (Tags Manual)
PUB 1756-021B-EN-P, (Parameters Manual)

Using Parameters for Buffering I/O:

1. Choose one of your programs and go to the *Parameters and Local Tags* folder.

2. Right-click and select the *Add New Parameter* option.

3. Create parameter associations for one or several of the digital inputs in the sample project.

FAULT-FINDING & RECOVERY:

Faults, are conditions that cause a PLC or PAC controller to suspend execution of its program logic and to shut-down. While at times controllers may be reset by cycling a key switch to Program and back into run mode, this is very often not the case. The first step in resolving a fault is to go online with the controller to view its **fault code** status. To do this, right-click on **Controller** inside the Controller Organizer, and go into the Controller Properties menu. From the Controller Properties menu select either the **Major Faults** or **Minor Faults** tabs to view a current fault condition. Many times a fault can be cleared from within this properties menu as well.

It's possible to automatically recover from some fault conditions, and allow program execution to resume without the controller ever going into an active fault state. This is accomplished by the use of a fault routine – but before we consider how to program a fault routine, let's first let's look at faults in general.

Within the ControlLogix family of controllers, faults fall into four general categories.

1. A **Major Fault** will trigger bits in the **MajorFaultRecord** attribute which, if not cleared, will stop the controller from executing routines, taking it out of run mode. Major Faults are sub-categorized into those that are **recoverable** and those that are **non-recoverable**. Recoverable major faults are those types of faults that can be corrected and cleared by some form of fault routine. After the fault routine is executed, normal processing can resume. An unrecoverable fault would be those types of faults created by hardware or connection failure, corrupted memory or communications faults. There are fault **types** and **codes** which are associated with different faults; an active code is held in the **MajorFaultRecord** attribute of the

Program object. Here are a just few examples of major fault types and codes (type#, code#) encountered in ControlLogix projects:

Example Types & Codes (type, code):

- JMP to a non-existent Label: (4, 42)
- Watch-dog timer fault: (6, 1)
- I/O module connection failure: (3, 16)
- Negative Timer value PRE or ACC: (4, 34)

Of these specific faults, some may be recoverable by running a fault routine that checks for the specific type and code values, then clears and resets the **MajorFaultRecord** attribute to zero values.

2. A **Minor Fault** will trigger bits in the **MinorFaultRecord** attribute. For the most part, these allow the controller to continue its execution of a program. Just like the fault types and codes that can be viewed for major faults, those for the minor fault category can be viewed, checked for by program logic, cleared and reset. Here are a few of those (type, code) designations, just to get a general idea.

    - RPI update overlap (3, 94)
    - Arithmetic Overflow (4, 4)
    - PID Setpoint out of range (4, 36)
    - Periodic Task Overlap (6, 2)
    - Battery Needs to be Replaced (10, 10).

3. An **I/O Fault** indicates a problem with an I/O module and can trigger a major fault if the module is configured to do so. If online with the processor the specific fault code and description can be seen by going to I/O Configuration folder and then to Module Properties. Codes are listed by a hex number, for example:

    - #001: Connection to Module Failed
    - #000D: I/O map instance created where instance is already in use.

4. A **User-Defined Fault** is a fault condition which you define; to find, trap and correct for *specific* conditions of your choosing. It uses a *jump-to-subroutine* (JSR) instruction which is conditional on the program logic you place before it on the rung. The JSR then jumps to your specific fault routine, then clears and resets the logic conditions that created the fault.

Fault routines, just like in SLC-500 programming, are simply a means of correcting and clearing a fault before the processor suspends execution and shuts-down. At other times a fault routine can provide for a systematic shut-down or a safe start-up for equipment. For a complete listing and explanation of fault types and codes see PUB 1756-PM014J.

Placement of Fault Routines:

Fault routines can be placed in several areas within a project - depending on the type of faults you anticipate, and what you want to happen should they occur. Therefore, if you need to protect for a fault condition on a program instruction level, or when certain conditions occur - such as a valve being in an incorrect position – you could place a fault routine within a Program level of the project.

If you want to protect against shut-down because of a "Watch-dog Timer" or an "I/O Module Communication Failure", then the fault routine would be placed in the *Fault Handler* task at the Controller level.

If you need to protect against accidental power loss by specifying how the controller and system restarts when power is restored, your fault routine should be placed within the *Power-Up Handler*, also at the Controller level. What is evident, is that there is a great deal of versatility in how fault routines can be used, all dependent on the needs and requirements for safe practices, and protection for personnel and equipment.

Here is an example of the Controller Organizer where I've placed several fault routines. These are added by doing a right-click on *MainProgram, Fault Handler*, or *Power-Up Handler*; you can then make the selection for adding a *New Program* and *New Routine*.

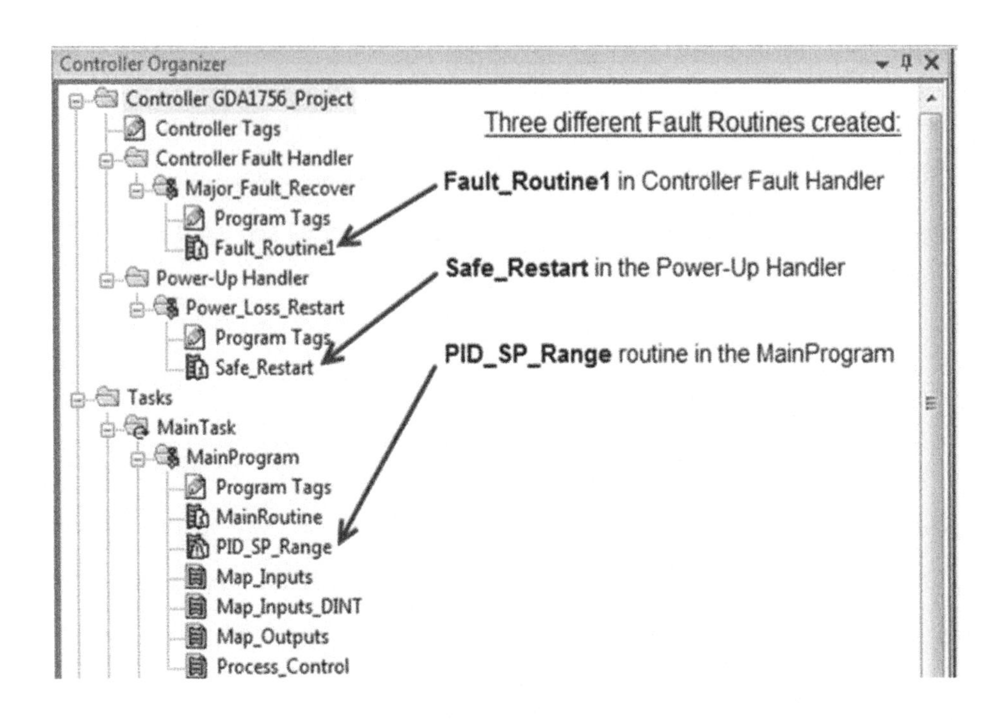

From this point, you name the routine, give it a description, designate the programming type (ladder diagram), assign it to a program and assign the routine as the fault routine. Once a routine is added to the project, you can program the routine to trap, correct and clear faults, and whatever control functions that may be necessary for your specific application.

Next shown is the *New Routine* configuration menu for one of the fault routines. This is the **Safe_Restart** routine in the **Power_Loss_Restart** program - within the **Power-Up Handler** task. If there is *not* a fault routine program in the Power-Up Handler, and power is lost and restored, the processor will not attempt to restart. It will shut-down with a major fault, (type 1, code 1) until cleared, and cycled back into RUN or Remote RUN mode.

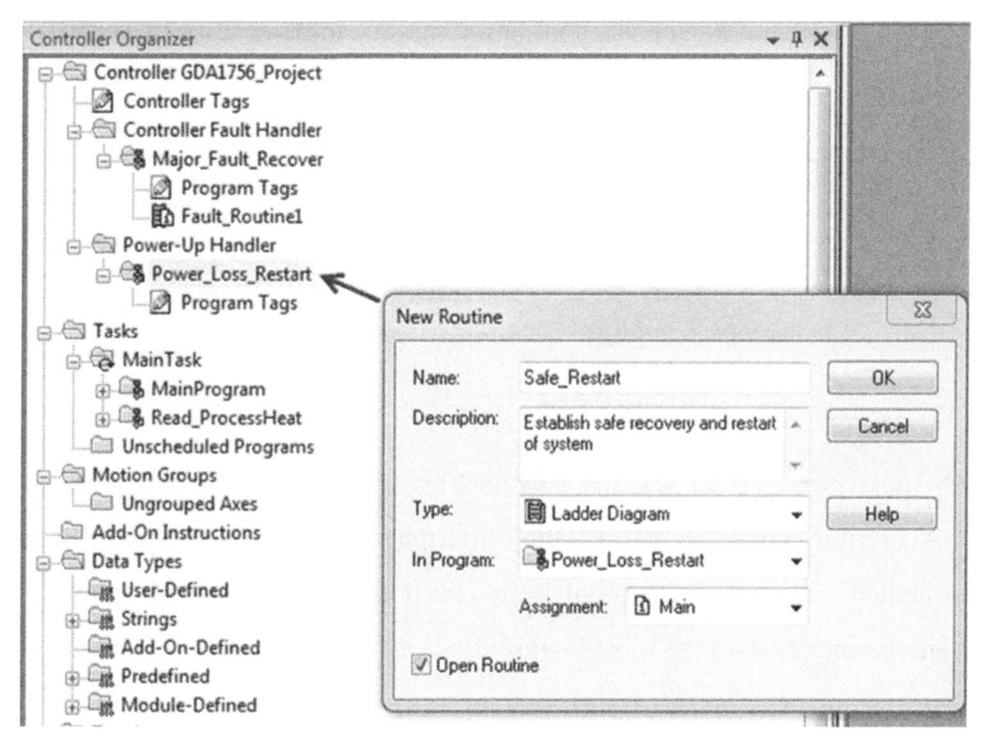

THE GSV AND SSV INSTRUCTIONS:

You recall that the SLC-500 platform had the status file (S2), from which different word elements or bits could be monitored and used in ladder programming, such as S:1/15 the first pass bit, or the S:13 and S14 math register. You could also look into the S2 data file for specific fault bits and codes – such as the S: 5 minor error bits, the S: 1/13 major fault bit, and the fault codes contained in the word element S: 6.

Fault status, along with specific fault types and codes can be obtained in the ControlLogix platform as well, although the method of doing so is slightly different.

In the ControlLogix platform, system information is contained in memory allocations referred to as **objects** – each with different **attributes** that contain system information, including fault information. This attribute information can be accessed from within the program by using two different instructions in the Studio 5000 instruction set.

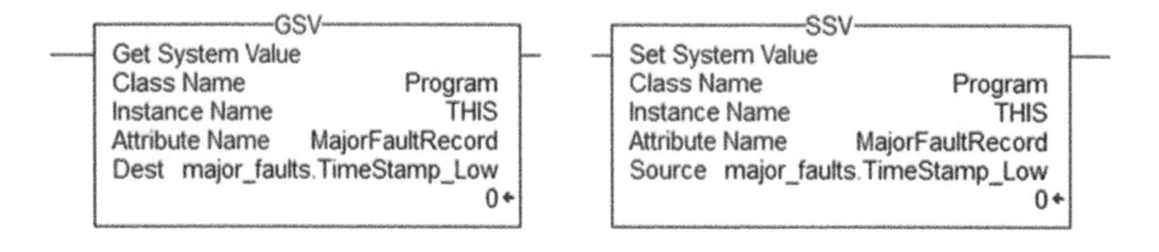

The GSV (get system value) and the SSV (set system value) are instructions used to obtain system information, in this case fault information, and then reset the system to a new "un-faulted" value once the problem has been cleared. So as you can see, these instructions are integral parts of most fault routines used in ControlLogix projects. Let's take one instruction at a time, look into what it does, and show how it would be used in a fault recovery process. The basic instruction descriptions are illustrated in the examples that follow:

The GSV instruction ***gets*** data from a **system object** (Class Name), and specifically from the **attributes** within the object, which you select. There are many different system objects in the Studio 5000 development platform, each with a number of attributes which vary from object to object. For instance, the *Program* object shown in the instructions above contains three attributes –the *Disable Flag*, the *LastScanTime*, and the *MajorFaultRecord* attributes. Another object, the *FaultLog* contains three, and the *MotionGroup* object contains eighteen. These attributes can be accessed by the GSV and SSV instructions for the data they hold. For a complete list of ControlLogix Objects, Attributes, and their characteristics, go to the Rockwell Automation library for PUB 1756-RM003.

Of these objects, the **Program** object and its attribute **MajorFaultRecord** are probably the most commonly used and relevant to fault detection and recovery. So the GSV shown above, will get the data contained in the *MajorFaultRecord* attribute, and write it into our chosen destination tag. I've created and named this destination tag: *major_faults*, it is structured after a user-defined data type (UDT) which I've created for this purpose. The SSV takes corrected values and writes them back into the *MajorFaultRecord* attribute. Note that when programming these instructions, if you click into the **Class Name** field, all the objects are shown in the drop-down menu for your selection. Likewise, once an object has been selected, the next fields, **Instance Name** and **Attribute Name**, will present options that are linked to that specific object. In our scenario we've selected the *MajorFaultRecord* as the attribute from which we want to obtain data.

The general flow of logic for the complete fault recovery routine will be as follows: *get the system data* (GSV), *compare it to a specific fault code* (EQU), if the fault matches the specific one for which we are checking then *clear the fault data* (CLR), and *set the corrected data* back into the *MajorFaultRecord* attribute by using the (SSV) instruction. Before going into further discussion of fault routine logic, let's take a brief look into Rockwell's recommended practice for accessing the data in the *MajorFaultRecord* attribute – this involves the creation and use of a *User-Defined* data type.

CREATE A USER-DEFINED DATA TYPE:

I've briefly mentioned user-defined data types (UDTs) in an earlier section, so you may recall that they are user-defined data structures containing multiple members of mixed data types. In addition, a UDT can be *associated with and referenced*, by a tag name.

Here we can use the UDT as the structure for obtaining data from a system attribute called *MajorFaultRecord*; but as we go through this example you'll hopefully discover other areas where a UDT would be useful. UDT's can be used for allocating or defining memory, with member names that are related to a specific aspect of a project, such as the control of different motors, or moving values into various processes or recipes.

As mentioned earlier, for this example we need to obtain data values from *MajorFaultRecord*, which is defined as a DINT[11] array. To do so, we need to create a UDT that matches the data structure used by this attribute. Note that a DINT[11] is a one-dimensional array of eleven 32 bit memory allocations. We can then create a new base tag, define it by the UDT data type we've just created, and write data to the tag in our fault routine.

To build this UDT, go to the Controller Organizer and right-click on the *User-Defined* heading under *Data Types*. Select the *New Data Type* option and the following dialog menu is displayed.

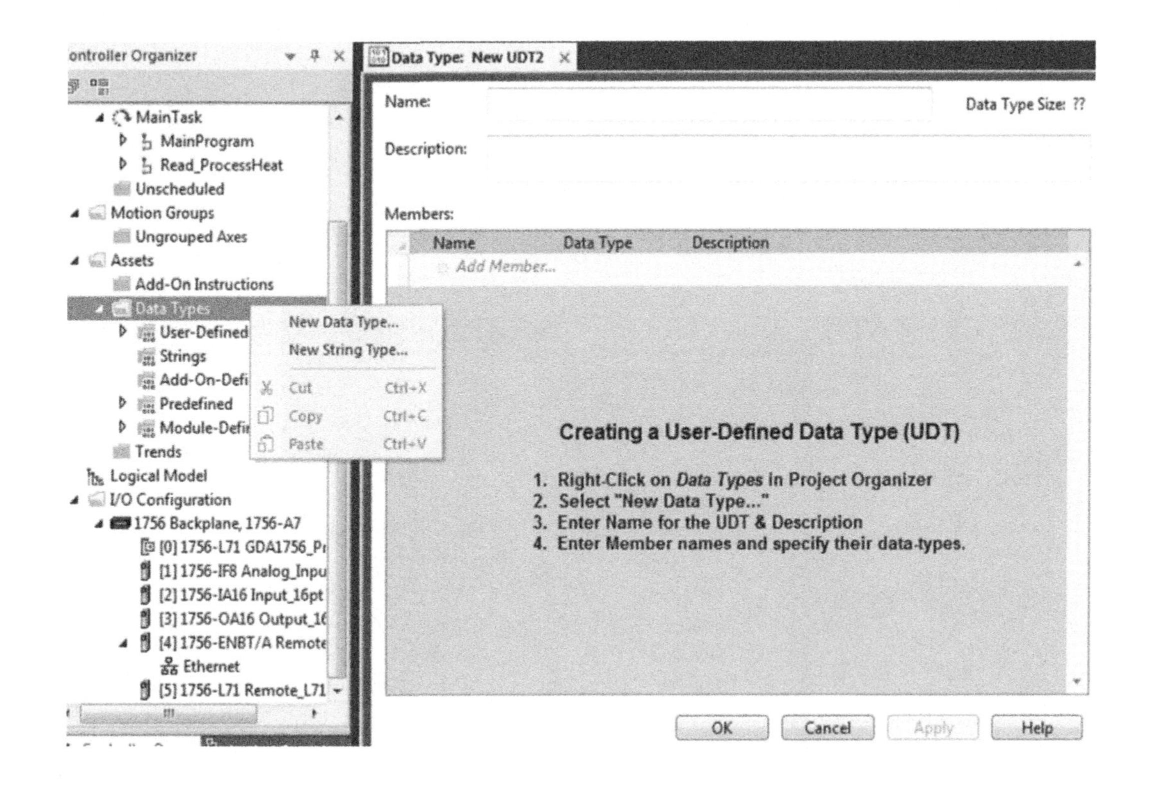

Give the UDT a name –I've used the name "FAULTS_MAJOR", a description (optional), and type in member names, defining each as shown. Remember, the MajorFaultRecord attribute is defined as DINT[11], meaning eleven double-integers (44 bytes). *Member names* are flexible, for instance you might prefer *Type* rather than *Fault_Type*, but they need to be defined as shown – in terms of their individual data-types. This accounts for the total eleven DINTs needed to accommodate our data.

The structural make-up of our desired attribute is important for the following reason. Because we will test for fault *type* and *code* within the fault routine, we need to know where in the larger block of memory, the DINT[11] array, this data is located. If we know this, we can designate a *member name* in the UDT, and reference that name specifically in the fault routine we create.

The following shows the newly created UDT named "FAULTS_MAJOR", and the fields associated with each member name and member data type. Notice that we've built a UDT structure comprising a total of DINT[11] or 44 bytes of memory.

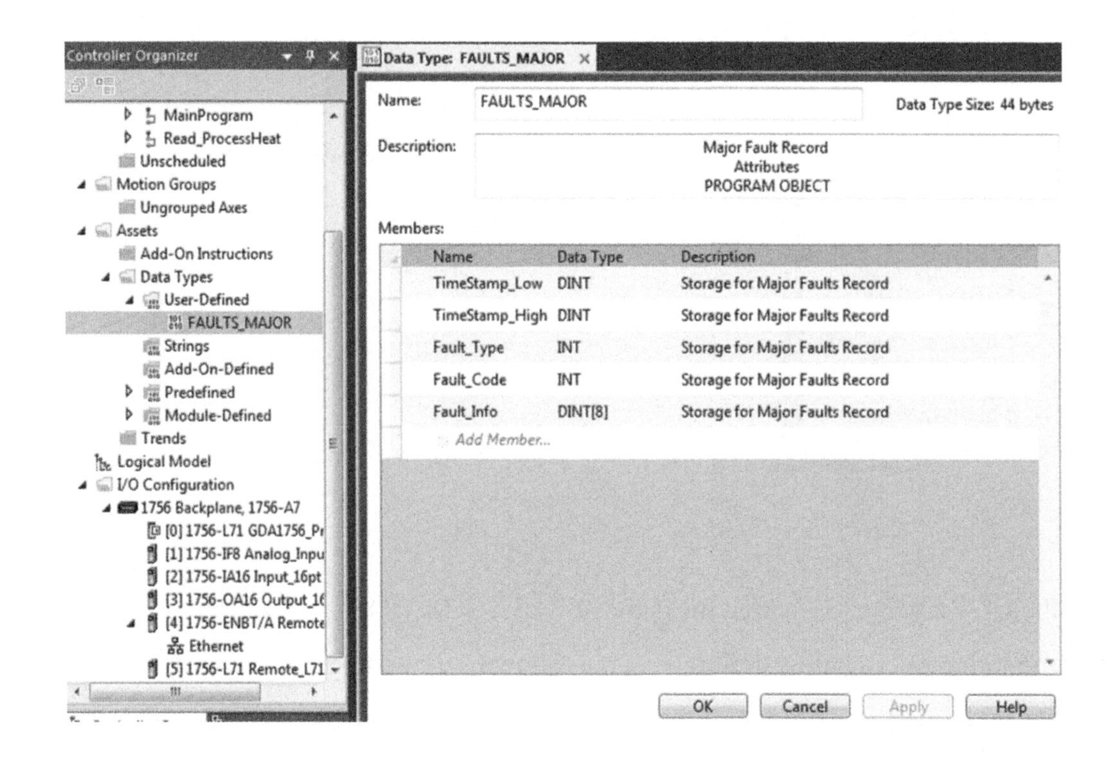

At this point we are ready to create a tag which can be used in the fault recovery routine. By defining it as the data type we've just created – the UDT called "FAULTS_MAJOR", we can now retrieve and place into it, the information we get from the object attribute MajorFaultRecord.

CREATING A TAG FOR THE UDT:

Next, go to the *Tag Editor* and create a tag to utilize this new data type. Remember, you enter the name at the bottom in the name field, I've used the name **major_faults** for the tag name; then when you select the *data type* for the new tag – select "FAULTS_MAJOR", our newly created UDT, from the dropdown list. It will now be shown along with many other data types.

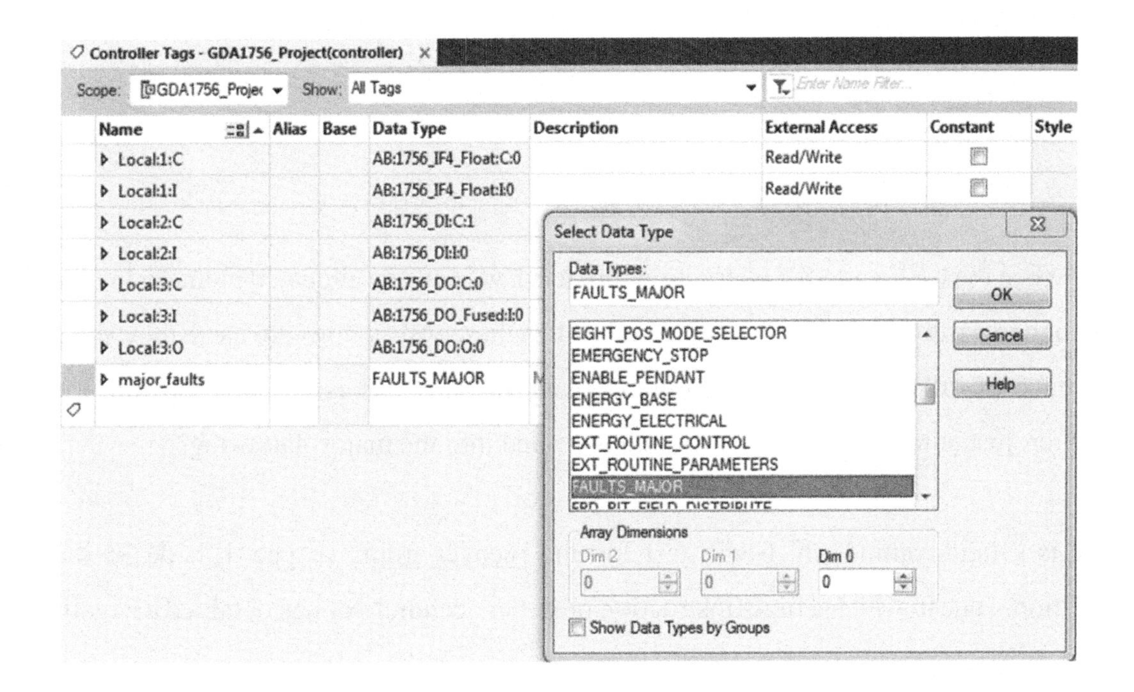

After you have created this new tag and linked (defined) it with your UDT data structure, you would see the following if you go to the *Tag Monitor* screen and expand the *major_faults* tag.

As you can see, all of the member elements you created as part of your UDT structure are now prefaced with the newly created tag name.

◢ major_faults			FAULTS_MAJOR	Major Fault Record Attributes ...
▷ major_faults.TimeStamp_Low			DINT	Major Fault Record Attributes ...
▷ major_faults.TimeStamp_High			DINT	Major Fault Record Attributes ...
▷ major_faults.Fault_Type			INT	Major Fault Record Attributes ...
▷ major_faults.Fault_Code			INT	Major Fault Record Attributes ...
▷ major_faults.Fault_Info			DINT[8]	Major Fault Record Attributes ...

Now when the GSV and SSV instructions are used, we have an allocated memory location in which to write and retrieve information. When these instructions are used, they should reference the attribute from its *beginning* block of data, this is the **TimeStamp_Low** member, just note that the entire attribute is copied into the major_faults tag.

Here is a fault routine which will test for and recover from, a type 4, code 34 fault condition – one in which a timer instruction preset or accumulator has obtained a negative value.

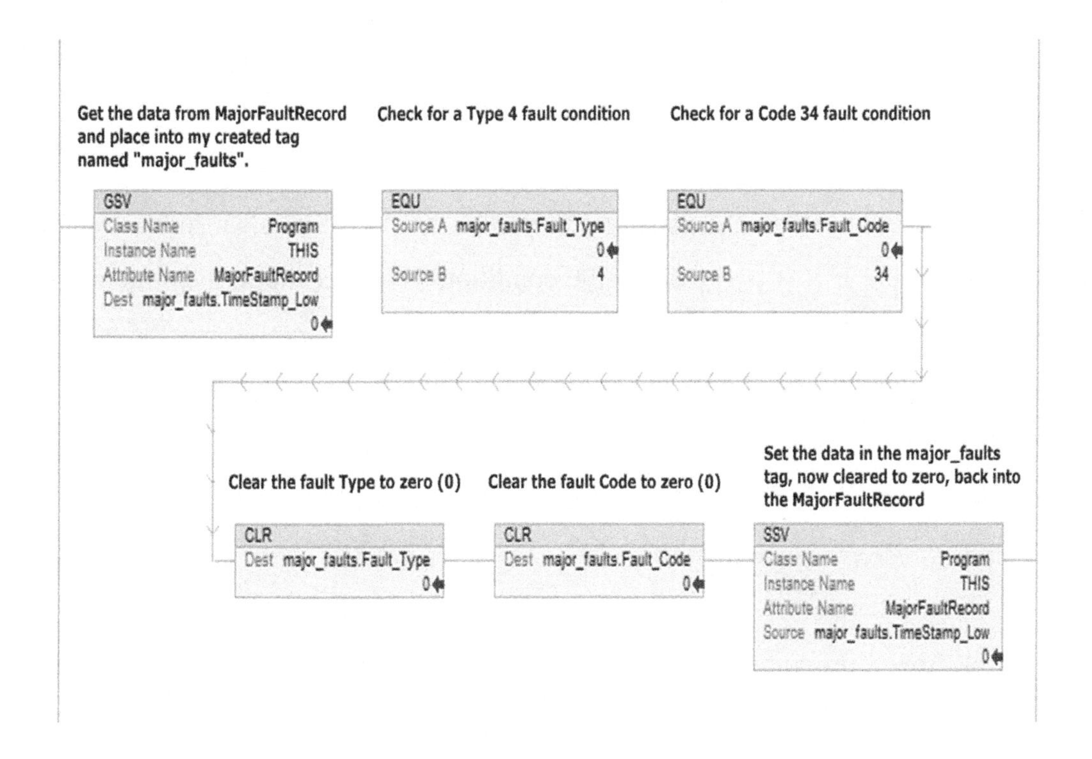

In order to test and recover from other types of faults, this same code could be repeated within the fault routine by adding EQU instructions for other types of fault codes. The GSV has already obtained the *MajorFaultRecord* attribute, so this instruction need not be repeated, but many other fault conditions could be tested and cleared, or alarm flags set from within the same routine.

USER-DEFINED FAULTS:

It's possible to create fault routines that deal with specific conditions, unique to your application or process. Such a condition might apply to a valve position, a blockage or breakdown on a conveyor system, or any number of things that can be programmed into ladder logic. The controller handles a user-defined fault just like any other major fault:

it suspends the execution of the logic program, and output modules are set to their configuration values.

The user-defined fault routine is usually initiated by the use of a JSR instruction within the program. If the JSR is triggered by the conditions that precede it, then the program jumps to the subroutine designated by name and by the input parameter that identifies it as a user-defined fault, the code numbers 990 through 999. If using a fault routine like the one shown above, you could test for a user-defined fault by using type 4 and then the user-defined codes within *compare instructions* that will test for specific faults. Note that *user-defined faults are always type 4.*

So, to break from a program routine based on a specific problem condition, and moving directly into a fault routine, requires the use of a JSR. This would be programmed directly into another routine where the Conveyor_Shutdown condition would be monitored. If triggered, program execution would jump to the fault routine named in the JSR.

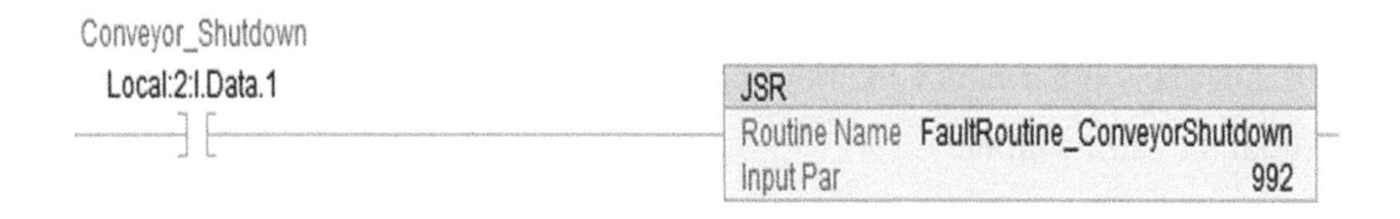

This fault routine might provide for recovery, or possibly just set alarm flags for an operator or other personnel, leaving the controller in a faulted state until the conditions that triggered the fault routine can be found and repaired.

Here is an example of set-up and usage:

- Under the Fault Handler task, right-click on the program and add *New Routine*. Select a name and add the other details for the new fault routine. Click OK.
- Program the logic for the fault routine.
- Configure the main program to use the fault routine by using the jump-to-subroutine (JSR).

POWER-UP HANDLER:

The last thing I'd like to show in this section is an example of a fault routine that might be used within the Power-Up Handler. Anytime power is lost to the controller and then restored, the controller defers to this task to run its routine – if one is available. Remember that if no routine is placed into this task and you experience a power loss, the controller will be in a fault state (type 1, code 1) whenever power is restored. Of course, this may be exactly the state you want for a particular control application; yet for other applications, specific conditions may need to be met when bringing equipment back to safe run state. This can often be accomplished by the use of a fault routine in the Power-Up Handler.

The Power-Up Handler can be used to clear the existing fault (1, 1), and then begin executing other instructions within the routine that will cause equipment or processes to be in a ready-for-operation state. To begin creating a power-up routine, much like any other routine in ControlLogix, you right-click on the Power-Up Handler task folder located in the Controller Organizer. Select the *New Program* option and name your new program, then right-click on the program you've just created and select the *New Routine* option. Name your new routine, select it as a ladder diagram, and assign it as Main.

Next, I've entered the following ladder logic in the new fault routine, and once again used the UDT we named "FAULTS_MAJOR" as the data type. This gives us a tag name; **major_faults**, we can use in retrieving information from the attribute, *MajorFaultRecord* of the *Program Object*. Here is the simple routine that will clear the type (1, 1) fault.

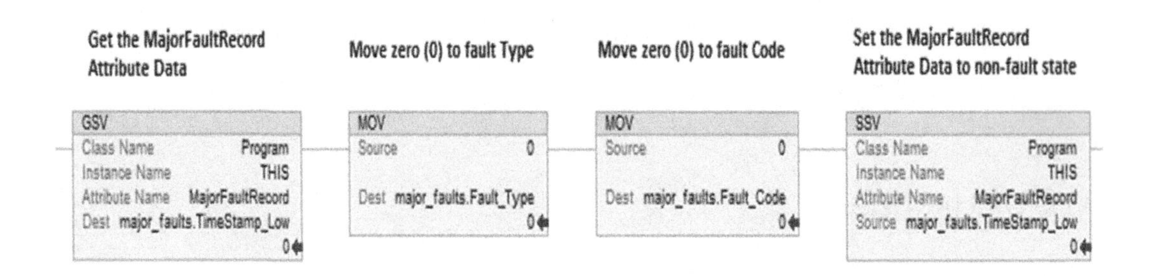

After this rung, other rungs and instructions could be added that would perform other operations such as initiate a power-up timing sequence, reset specific counters, allow power back on for critical equipment, or restart hydraulic and cooling systems.

The loss of power on equipment and control systems, present unique situations and opportunities for the use of a power-up fault routine. What will be the state of the equipment if power fails? Motor drives, hydraulic pumps, proportional control valves, solenoid valves that operate a press; all of these are examples of the types of controlled systems which might experience problems in the event of a random power loss. These thoughts and questions are crucial in addressing concerns on how to bring a system back up once power is restored. For this reason, every control scenario merits careful consideration upon all the safety factors that protect personnel and prevent unnecessary damage to equipment.

Concluding Remarks:

I believe the topics we've covered in this short book, represent many of the fundamental and practical skills we need to effectively program and troubleshoot these controllers. While the term fundamental may apply - it doesn't mean these concepts are necessarily simple or easy to master. Nor is it always easy to understand how another person has programmed a particular project. ControlLogix gives us a great deal of flexibility in putting together a project, with many ideas and new concepts to learn. So a good understanding of these topics can make the use of Studio 5000 software and its elements easier and more enjoyable to use. I hope this book has helped bring together some of the more unwieldy aspects of using Studio 5000 Logix Designer.

As I've said before, I know you have many options when choosing books and online resources that discuss these topics; so I thank you for selecting my book – and I hope you feel you've benefited by doing so.

As always, I welcome your comments and feedback. My goal is to present, in simple and clear language, relevant technical topics, and I have found feedback from my readers a valuable resource. If you would like to contact me with questions or comments you can do so at the following email address or website:

GaryAndersonBooks.com

Email: ganderson61@cox.net

Your reviews on Amazon are helpful and appreciated. If you've enjoyed what you've read and feel this book has provided a positive benefit to you, then please take a moment and write a short review.

Other books by Gary Anderson

GaryAndersonBooks.com

Practical Guides for the Industrial Technician:

Motion Control for CNC & Robotics
Variable Frequency Drives – Installation & Troubleshooting
Industrial Network Basics

RSLogix 500 Programming Series:

Basics Concepts of Ladder Logic Programming
Advanced Programming Concepts
Ladder Logic Diagnostics & Troubleshooting
PID Programming Using RS Logix 500
Program Flow Instructions Using RS Logix 500

Studio 5000 Logix Designer
A Learning Guide for ControlLogix Basics

Made in the USA
Monee, IL
13 July 2023